The Pictorial Encyclopedia of Fishes

The Pictorial Encyclopedia of Fishes

S. Frank

Consultant: Alwyne Wheeler

British Museum, Natural History

Hamlyn

London · New York · Sydney · Toronto

Translated by Helga Hanks
Designed and produced by Artia for
The Hamlyn Publishing Group Limited
London • New York • Sydney • Toronto
Hamlyn House, Feltham, Middlesex, England
© Copyright 1969 Artia, Prague
Translation © Copyright 1971
The Hamlyn Publishing Group Limited
Reprinted 1972

ISBN 0 600 36946 3

Printed in Czechoslovakia by Svoboda, Prague

FOREWORD

Fishes present a curious paradox in that they are both well known and unknown. They are well known because they are familiar in everyday life: in the fishmarket and the kitchen, in the aquarium and the garden pool, to the child with a dip net and to the angler. Yet we know so little about them that previously unrecognized species are described by the dozen each year. The relationships of many even well known kinds are still in dispute, and new facts and discoveries emerge almost daily.

This is, of course, partly because fishes live in a medium alien to ourselves and they are by no means easy to observe as living animals. While it is true that fishes were kept in semi-captivity in mediaeval times in Europe – mainly with a culinary product in mind – the initiative in live fish culture lay with the contemporary Chinese, although owing to cultural barriers we know too little about the early history of their art. Truly scientific aquarium keeping is barely 120 years old, and thus observation of healthy, living fishes in a reasonably natural habitat is a relatively recent development. Even more recent are the techniques of underwater television and deep-sea photography, observation from submersible vessels and the sport of fish watching by SCUBA divers. In the years to come the world will learn many new facts about fish life from these sources.

Dr Stanislav Frank's book represents a considerable advance in fish books for it illustrates examples from the whole spectrum of this alien world. The accuracy of photography combined with the diversity of beautiful and always graceful living fishes makes it both a useful reference book and a pleasure to look through. The text comprises a volume of data concerning the habitat and geographical distribution of the fishes illustrated, with notes on their anatomy, ecology and sometimes breeding habits. That many of the fishes illustrated are aquarium kept specimens is no disadvantage for other wide-ranging books on aquarium fishes use photographs sparingly, and moreover Dr Frank, scientific assistant at the Zoological Institute in Prague, brings a wealth of personal experience to his subject. This, too, must be welcomed for another reason. The arts of fish keeping and fish culture have been brought to a high standard by central European workers, and information about their methods and successes is welcome; a book such as this bridges the gap created by language and ideological differences.

In this book the fishes and their families are related to their orders, and the whole gives a general outline of the classification of recent fishes. The arrangement may seem unfamiliar to many readers but in general it follows that formulated in 1940 by Dr Leo S. Berg, a Russian ichthyologist and zoogeographer of international repute. Whatever the classification adopted, whether it is familiar or not, nothing can be more interesting than the living fishes. They know few limits to their aquatic world, for they are found in hill-streams amongst the rushing torrent, and at the bottom of the deep trenches of the oceans, sometimes under five miles of water. The worst barriers they meet are those erected by man with pollution and the development of waterways. In size fishes range from the gigantic, such as the Whale Shark of tropical waters, a veritable giant 14 metres (45 ft) long, to the miniature Tetras of the Amazon no more than 4 cm (1½ in) in length. Their coloration, so often thought to be drab by those who merely see them in the fishmarket, is a wonderful range of brilliant hues and delicate countershading to others who see fishes alive, while the variations in body form are legion. A book can merely bring a glimpse of this wonderful world of fishes but it is an introduction to a world that can with a little trouble be explored without end.

Alwyne Wheeler

INTRODUCTION

A brief outline of the anatomy, ecology and classification of fishes may help to clarify the text of this pictorial encyclopedia.

Most fishes are more or less streamlined in form, but a number of fishes have eel-shaped, flattened, or even practically spherical bodies. The shape of a fish is an indication of its adaptation to a particular habitat or mode of life. Streamlining entails the least resistance to movement through open water; forms which live on the bottom are generally flattened; slow-swimming fishes with rounded bodies are often protected by spines or armour plating.

The body of a fish is supported by its skeleton, consisting principally of a skull and a backbone. The backbone rarely contains more than 100 vertebrae and then only in the case of fishes with an eel-like body. The ribs afford some support to the body cavity in which lie the internal organs. The skull varies considerably: in Lampreys it consists of gristle and lacks jaws, while the most complex arrangement is found in Teleost fishes. Most fishes have teeth, either on the jaws or on bones further down in the pharynx.

Three main types of mouth formation are encountered: symmetrical [212], with projecting lower jaw [218], and with projecting upper jaw [227]. These are closely connected with the creature's feeding habits. The mouth is surrounded by folds of skin (lips), which in some fishes are very thick with hard edges and serve to rub algae off stones and water plants. In the Catfishes part of the mouth is adapted into a suction pad which attaches the fish to the bottom. At the corners of the mouth and on the lower jaw there are often barbels [349] which serve mainly as organs of touch and taste.

In very young fishes the fins are continuous and amorphous — only later do they become stiffened with bony fin rays. In the front part of the fin there are hard, unjointed fin rays which are sometimes developed as spines and may form a separate spiny fin. The remaining fin rays are called the soft fin rays — these are generally branched and made up of segments. Fins are either paired or unpaired. The paired fins are the pectoral fins (corresponding to the forelimbs of land-dwelling vertebrates) and the pelvic fins (corresponding to the hindlimbs). The dorsal fin or fins, the anal fin or fins, and the tail fin comprise the unpaired fins. Paired fins show remarkable variation in structure. The pectoral fins of the Climbing Perches are adapted for crawling along damp ground out of water. Some fishes have greatly enlarged pectoral fins, enabling them to glide over the water's surface. In male Sharks and Rays part of the pelvic fin complex is modified to form a pair of copulatory organs, the claspers, while in the Live-bearing Tooth-carps the intromittent organ of the male is a modified anal fin. An adipose fin — fatty and lacking in fin rays — is present on the back between the dorsal and tail fins in Salmons, Characins and some Catfishes.

Scales cover the bodies of most fishes. Sharks have placoid scales formed from small, enamel-covered teeth. Ganoid scales are flat, trapezoid plates of bone with a layer of hard, shiny secretion called ganoin. The Carp-like fishes have cycloid scales, which are large, thin, round bony plates. Similar to these are the comb-like ctenoid scales — round, flat plates with little teeth or spines on the hind part — which are seen to best advantage in the Perches. Both cycloid and ctenoid scales are arranged in regular rows and overlap like roof tiles. The Sturgeons, however, have a few rows of bony plates instead of scales. Many fishes, for example the Catfishes, are scaleless and covered with a thick skin.

Colouring is determined by a number of different pigmentation cells, which are mainly situated beneath the epidermis in the dermal layer of the skin. Cells causing the effect of iridescence, known as iridocytes, are situated in the lower layers of the dermis. Iridocytes contain an agglomeration of guanin crystals which reflect the light and so bring about the shimmering effect seen in the colour of so many fishes. Pigment cells are not distributed evenly over the whole body but are usually more concentrated on the belly and on the sides than on the back. In some individuals the phenomenon known as xanthism occurs — all pigment cells except the yellow and orange ones are absent. Xanthic specimens usually have black eyes. In cases of albinism no pigment cells are present in the skin and even the eyes are pink. Albinism is most common in Fighting Fishes, the Barbels and the Pikes.

Colouring and body form serve a protective function in many fishes. A clear example of this is the camouflage of the Australian Seahorse, *Phyllopteryx* eques, whose skin trails down in long, ragged fronds of brown and red. Many other fishes show adaptations of body colour to blend with the environment.

Fishes 'breathe' by ventilating their gills with a current of water. The gill arches bear a series of lamellae which are richly supplied with blood and serve to extract oxygen from the water. On the inside the arches are covered with a number of fine filaments or rakers. These may be important for filtering plankton from the water.

The swim-bladder of Bony Fishes is a hydrostatic organ. It arises embryonically from an enlargement of the back wall of the throat, while the lungs arise as an enlargement of the lower wall. Lungs are found only in the Bichirs and Lungfishes although some other fishes, such as the Climbing Perches, also have auxiliary air breathing organs. The embryonic connection between the throat and the swim-bladder remains open throughout life in some species, for example the Carps.

The majority of fishes lay eggs which are fertilized outside the body: only in the Sharks and the Live-bearing Tooth-carps does fertilization take place internally. The eggs of Sharks are laid either singly or in groups inside a hard egg case. The case is usually rectangular and has thread-like extensions at the corners which may attach the egg case to sea weeds. The eggs are normally large – those of some Sharks are over 22 cm (9 in) long. Many Sharks and some Rays are live-bearing.

Almost all fishes show a clear distinction between the sexes, but a few, such as the Sea Perches, are hermaphrodite. In some species this goes as far as self-fertilization, while in others the male and female sex organs develop at different times in the same individual. Sexual differences are often evident in features not directly related to reproductive function. Males may be distinguishable from females by the form and size of fins, the length of barbels or the position of the eyes. In the Carps, for example, the male often develops a spawning rash during the spawning season.

Fishes may be grouped according to their habitat. The Soviet marine biologist Nikolski divided them into sea-water fishes, fresh-water fishes, migratory fishes and brackish-water fishes (species living in river estuaries). Within these groupings further distinctions may be made. Pelagic fishes live in the open water near the surface, littoral forms live near the shore, benthonic forms keep to the sea floor, and the deep-sea, oceanic fishes either live in mid-water (bathyal) or near the bottom (abyssal). Fresh-water fishes living in the faster flowing waters of streams and rivers are known as rheophile, while those which inhabit lakes, pools and ponds are limnophile. There are two main types of migratory fishes; those which live in the sea and swim up river to spawn (anadromous migration) like the Salmon, and those which spend most of their life in fresh water and only swim down to the sea to spawn (catadromous migration) as in the case of the Eels.

Among the stranger modes of life adopted by fishes is that of the Remoras which attach themselves to Sharks by means of a suction disc. They feed on the parasites of their large companion and are also thought to scavenge. The close relationship between the Demoiselles and some sea anemones is also curious. These fishes can hide themselves among the poisonous tentacles of the anemone with impunity. Parasitism, although common in the Cyclostomes, is rare among the higher fishes. A small Catfish of the genus *Vandellia* lives parasitically in the gill cavity of larger Catfishes (*Sorubim* and *Platystoma*). Its narrow body enables it to slip under the gill cover of its host where it feeds on blood drawn from wounds which it inflicts with a spine on its own gill covers.

Finally the system of naming and classifying fishes needs an explanation. Each type, or species, has two names. The **Salmon**, for example, is known under the scientific name *Salmo salar*. The first name, *Salmo*, is the generic name and is shared by a number of other species. Thus *Salmo trutta*, the **Sea Trout**, and *Salmo gairdneri*, the **Rainbow Trout**, belong to the same genus. The second name, *salar*, is the specific name and is peculiar to the Salmon, just as *trutta* and *gairdneri* denote specifically the Sea Trout and the Rainbow Trout. Where a species exists in more than one form, a further name may be added to indicate the subspecies. The **Grayling**, *Thymallus thymallus*, has a subspecies, *Thymallus thymallus lacustris*, which is found in large lakes. As species are grouped together into genera, so genera are placed together in families: *Salmo*, *Oncorhynchus* and *Salvelinus* belong to the family Salmonidae. Families can be further grouped into suborders and orders. The suborder Salmonoidei contains the families Salmonidae, Thymallidae, etc. and the order Clupeiformes includes in addition to the Salmonoidei, the Clupeoidei (Herrings and Tarpons), Esocoidei (Pikes) and so on. These groups are drawn up on the basis of common characteristics. They are necessarily somewhat arbitrary and are the subject of dispute amongst ichthyologists, but it is broadly true that the genera within a family are more similar to one another than to genera in other families and that the families within an order resemble each other more closely than they resemble other families. These similarities have not arisen by accident — they are the result of an evolution from common ancestral forms — and it is the aim of modern systems of classification to reflect as accurately as present knowledge will allow the evolutionary relationships between the various groups of fishes.

SYSTEMATIC CLASSIFICATION OF LIVING FISHES

Phylum: Chordata (Chordates)
Subphylum: Craniata/Vertebrata (Vertebrates)
Superclass: Agnatha (Jawless Fishes)
Class: Cyclostomata
    Order: Petromyzoniformes (Lampreys)
    Order: Myxiniformes (Hagfishes)
Superclass: Gnathostomata (Jawed Fishes)
Class: Elasmobranchii
    Order: Selachii (Sharks)
      Suborder: Heterodontoidea
      Suborder: Galeoidea
    Order: Batoidei (Rays)
      Suborder: Torpedinoidei (Electric Rays)
      Suborder: Rajoidei (Skates and Rays)
      Suborder: Myliobatoidei (Stingrays)
Class: Holocephali
    Order: Chimaeriformes (Rabbitfishes)
Class: Dipnoi (Lungfishes)
    Order: Ceratodiformes (Australian Lungfishes)
    Order: Lepidosireniformes (African and South American Lungfishes)
Class: Osteichthyes/Teleostomi (Bony Fishes)
    Subclass: Crossopterygii
      Order: Coelacanthiformes (Coelacanths)
    Subclass: Actinopterygii (Ray-finned Fishes)
      Order: Polypteriformes (Bichirs and Reed-fishes)
    Subclass: Chondrostei
      Order: Acipenseriformes (Sturgeons)
      Order: Amiiformes (Bowfins)
      Order: Lepisosteiformes (Garpikes)
    Subclass: Teleostei (recent Bony Fishes)
      Order: Clupeiformes
        Suborder: Clupeoidei (Tarpons and Herrings)
        Suborder: Phractolaemoidei
        Suborder: Salmonoidei (Salmons and Trouts)
        Suborder: Esocoidei (Pikes)
        Suborder: Osteoglossoidei (Bony Tongues)
        Suborder: Pantodontoidei (Butterfly Fishes)
      Order: Mormyriformes
      Order: Cypriniformes
        Suborder: Characinoidei (Characins)
        Suborder: Gymnotoidei (Knife-fishes)
        Suborder: Cyprinoidei (Carps)
        Suborder: Siluroidei (Catfishes)
      Order: Anguilliformes (Eels)
      Order: Beloniformes (Garfishes)
      Order: Gadiformes (Cods)
      Order: Gasterosteriformes (Sticklebacks)
      Order: Syngnathiformes (Pipefishes)
      Order: Cyprinidontiformes (Tooth-carps)
      Order: Beryciformes (Soldierfishes)
      Order: Mugiliformes (Grey Mullets)
      Order: Ophicephaliformes (Snakeheads)
      Order: Perciformes
        Suborder: Percoidei (Perches)
        Suborder: Blennioidei (Blennies)
        Suborder: Siganoidei
        Suborder: Acanthuroidei (Surgeonfishes)
        Suborder: Scombroidei (Mackerels)
        Suborder: Anabantoidei (Labyrinth-fishes)
        Suborder: Luciocephaloidei (Pike-heads)
        Suborder: Gobioidei (Gobies)
        Suborder: Cottoidei (Bullheads)
      Order: Dactylopteriformes (Flying Gurnards)
      Order: Thunniformes (Tunnies)
      Order: Pleuronectiformes (Flatfishes)
      Order: Mastacembeliformes (Spiny Eels)
      Order: Echeneiformes (Remoras)
      Order: Tetraodontiformes (Triggerfishes and Pufferfishes
      Order: Gobiesociformes (Clingfishes)
      Order: Lophiiformes (Anglerfishes)

The first few photographs in this encyclopedia bear only a remote resemblance to the conventional idea of a fish. They illustrate two curious groups of eel-like creatures, the Lampreys (Petromyzones) and Hagfishes (Myxini), which in terms of evolution are closely related to the fishes, but which, even though they have common ancestors, differ greatly in appearance from the fishes as we usually conceive them. Their extraordinary appearance is largely due to the retention of primitive characteristics. Yet in a survey of fishes which begins with the simplest evolutionary forms and proceeds to the more complex, they should undoubtedly be considered first.

Both the groups referred to above belong to the superclass Agnatha (jawless fishes). They have eel-shaped bodies and lack paired pelvic and pectoral fins. The mouth has no jaws and is a simple opening; the skin is smooth and lacks scales. There is a single nostril in the mid-line on top of the front of the head.

The Agnatha are divided into two orders. The members of the first order, the Lampreys (Petromyzoniformes), are distinguished in the adult state by a round, disc-shaped mouth adapted for sucking, containing a number of horny teeth arranged in a typical pattern about the disc. They have a cylindrical body. Behind the head, along the sides of the body, there are seven pairs of

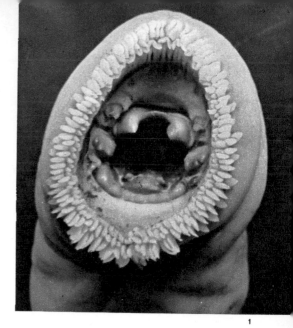

1

gills. The skeleton consists of a notochord with associated small blocks of cartilage; this does not form a true spine but protects the spinal chord in the same way as true vertebrae. The brain and heart have a similar protective covering of gristle.

Lampreys inhabit fresh water but migrate to the sea. They are found in temperate zones of both

2

3

northern and southern hemispheres. In the northern hemisphere only Lampreys of the subfamily **Petromyzoninae** are to be found. The **Lampern** or **River Lamprey,** *Lampetra fluviatilis*, grows to a length of 40–50 cm (16–20 in). The fully grown Lampern dwells in the seas of Europe, and related species live on the coasts of North America and Japan. It migrates up rivers and spawns in shallow gravel streams. Picture 1 shows the characteristic shape of the sucking disc and teeth.

The **Brook Lamprey,** *Lampetra planeri*, spends its entire life in fresh water. It is found widely in western Europe. It grows to a length of 10–16 cm (4–6 in), and migrates only locally within its home stream. In spring, when the ice melts and the

4

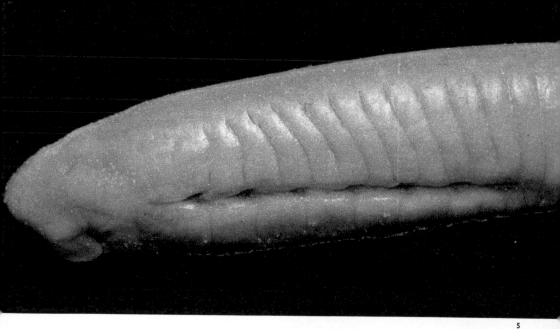

water becomes warmer, the sexually mature Brook Lampreys breed provided that the water temperature is between 8 and 12°C. Both males and females hang on to rocks with their sucking discs and with their tails hollow out a circular depression in the sand or gravel of the river bed.

They lift the larger stones out of the hollow with their mouths in order to make the nest ready [2], while sand or mud is disturbed by their activity and is washed downstream.

Spawning takes place with the female attached to a rock by the mouth. The male may also cling to the rock, while folding his body around that of the female [3]. Sometimes he fastens onto the front of the female [4]. The tube-shaped urogenital papilla of the male is not in fact an organ of insemination, for the eggs are fertilized in the water as they are shed by the female. The larvae remain buried after hatching for between four and six years in the river bed or among detritus along the bank. A cursory examination reveals some differences between immature and adult specimens: in the young Lamprey a groove connects the gill holes [5], there is a vestigial line of fins, the mouth is shaped like a horseshoe with distinct upper and lower lips [6], and the eyes are completely covered by skin. During its larval life the Lamprey feeds on decaying organic matter, in particular plant remains and micro-organisms sifted from the surrounding mud and water.

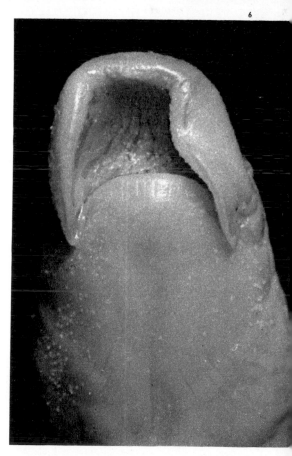

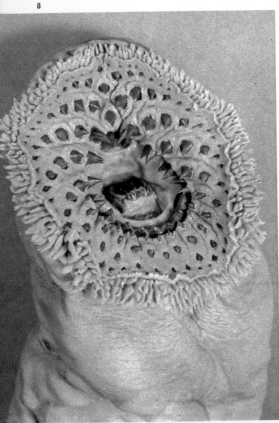

The **Sea Lamprey**, *Petromyzon marinus* [7], grows
to a length of 90 cm (36 in). It is found on both
European and North American coasts of the
Atlantic and in fresh water. The Sea Lamprey swims
upstream to spawn (anadromous migration), and
can shift stones weighing over 1 kg (2 lb) while
hollowing out its nest, which it sites in a strong
current. The larvae are similar to those of the
Brook Lamprey. Specimens caught at the time of
their metamorphosis are 10–20 cm (4–8 in) long.
The adults live parasitically on other fishes. They
attach themselves to their victims by the suction
disc of the mouth [8], and bore a hole in the
body of the host with their file-like tongues. They
feed principally by sucking in the blood which
flows from the wound, or liquidized flesh which is
formed by the action of secretions from the
glands in the mouth and the rasping of the tongue.
If the host dies, the Lamprey leaves it and goes off
in search of another. The parasitic phase lasts for
a year or eighteen months. Lampreys tend to dwell
in deeper waters; the older, sexually mature
specimens can be found nearer the shore and in
estuaries. When the Sea Lamprey entered the
North American Great Lakes it proved to be
a serious predator of the native fishes.

The second order of the Agnatha comprises the
Hagfishes, **(Myxiniformes).** They are entirely
sea fishes. To the family **Bdellostomatidae**
belongs the genus *Bdellostoma*, whose members have

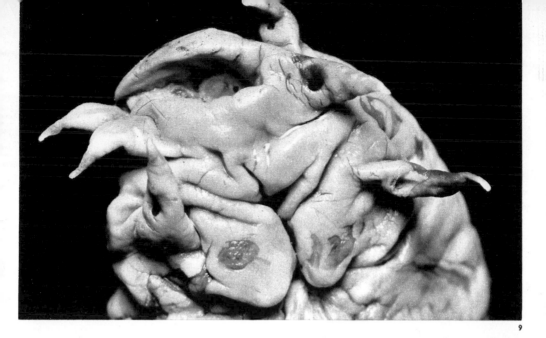

between five and eight gill holes. Various species live on the coasts of California, Chile, and Japan. The mouth is encircled with barbels [9]. The **Hagfish**, *Myxine glutinosa*, lives in coastal waters of the Atlantic Ocean; it grows to a length of 50 cm (20 in) and is placed in a separate family, **Myxinidae**. Its mouth [10] is similar to that of the species already described. It lives at depths of 18–300 m (60–1,000 ft), but has been recorded as deep as 900 m (3,300 ft). It is greatly detested by fishermen, for it attacks fishes that are already in the net and so have little scope for movement and none for escape; it sucks out the flesh of the fishes and so lowers the value of the catch. Up to 125 Hagfishes have been counted attacking a single Cod. Hagfishes also eat a variety of bottom-living invertebrates, but it is not known if these are dead when eaten. They die fairly swiftly if kept in aquaria, for they are adapted to living at a depth of at least 18 m (60 ft). However, if they are kept in cold water at a suitably high pressure, they will survive even in captivity for several weeks. They owe their alternative name Slime-eels to their ability to secrete large quantities of slime when provoked. This slime enables the creature to live within the body of the host, by protecting it from the host's digestive juices within the stomach. Two or three of these creatures can turn a bucket of water into a gelatinous liquid in a short time. Hagfishes have no economic value.

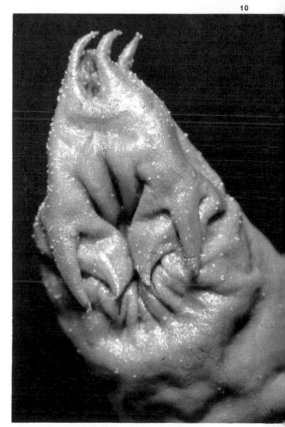

11

12

13

The second superclass of vertebrates comprises
the fishes with jaws, the Gnathostomata. These are
divided into four classes: the **Elasmobranchii**
(Sharks and Rays), the **Holocephali** (Rabbitfishes),
the **Dipnoi** (Lungfishes), and finally the **Teleostomi** (Bony Fishes), to which the majority of all
species of fishes belong.
The only living Elasmobranchs are the **Selachii**
(Cartilaginous Fishes). They have well-developed
fins, and jaws with a characteristic skeletal structure, usually set well back on the underside of the
head. The skeleton is cartilaginous, although
often calcified, and the branchial skeleton is a series of separate gill arches with corresponding
gill slits on the sides of the body just behind the
head. Some sharks are viviparous while others lay
eggs. Their distribution is world-wide, and more

than 250 species are recognized. The suborder
Heterodontoidea comprises the most primitive
of sharks. They have two dorsal fins, with a spine
on the leading edge, and there are five gill slits.
Remains of members of this order have been found
dating from the Upper Jurassic. Today, however,
only a few species survive and they live in the
Pacific and Indian Oceans. They keep to coastal
waters and feed principally on molluscs. Their
teeth are short, serrated and well adapted to
crunching up mussels and snails. The **Port Jackson
Shark,** Heterodontus philippi [11], is well known
on the coasts of Australia. It reaches a length of
up to 1.5 m (5 ft).

Among members of the family **Isuridae,** surborder
Galeoidea, the **White Shark,** Carcharodon

carcharias, is particularly dangerous to man with its teeth which may be up to 5 cm (2 in) long [13]. This Shark grows to a length of 13 m (40 ft). Closely related species, now extinct, are known from the bottom of the Upper Cretaceous through to the Pliocene. Some of them were as long as 30 m (100 ft) and the teeth alone were up to 13 cm (5 in) long. The White Shark is the species most often involved in attacks on man, and on occasions even small boats, entirely without provocation. It is for this reason that most Australian bathing beaches are protected by wire netting. Cases of fatal attacks by this species have also been recorded on the warmer coast of North America. Both the White Shark and the related **Mako,** *Isurus oxyrinchus* [12], are inhabitants of warm seas. The Mako, which is a well-known angler's Shark, grows to a length of 4 m (13 ft).

The **Fox Shark** or **Thresher Shark,** *Alopias vulpinus* [14], which belongs to the family **Alopii-**

dae, has an unusual tail fin: the top lobe is extended to a length as great as the rest of the body. It is said that the probable reason for this is that it uses its tail to deal stunning blows among schools of Herring and Sardines. It achieves a weight of 450 kg (990 lb) and a length of 6 m (20 ft).

15

16

edges form fleshy barbels. They are not dangerous to man. In spite of their considerable size – up to 6 or 7 m (19 to 23 ft) – they often provide sport for anglers. They are excellent swimmers, and are particularly abundant in the waters around Cuba and the West Indies.

Zebra Sharks, *Stegostoma fasciatum* [16], dwell in the Indo-Australian region. In youth they bear brightly coloured stripes, but the pattern tends to change with the years, until the fish has a flecked appearance, or until one colour disappears completely. Some members of the genus *Stegostoma* [17] are similar in size and shape to the European Dogfishes.

The genus *Hemiscyllium* has roughly the same area of distribution as *Stegostoma*. *Hemiscyllium plagiosum* [18] is sometimes kept in aquaria. This species, too, changes its colouring as it grows older.

Among the best known of the smaller species of Selachians are the Dogfishes (family **Scyliorhinidae**), especially the **Lesser Spotted Dogfish,** *Scyliorhinus caniculus* [19], which lives in the Mediterranean and the eastern Atlantic. It grows to a length of 1 m (3 ft) and is very common in British waters.

17

The Nurse Shark family **(Orectolobidae)** consists entirely of bottom-living sharks, which live in warm seas. Their principal area of distribution lies in the western part of the Pacific and the Indian Ocean. The species *Ginglymostoma cirratum* [15] is ovoviviparous. The nostrils of this species are connected to the mouth by a groove, whose front

In some seas the grey-coloured **Smooth Hound,** *Mustelus asterias*, which belongs to the family **Triakidae**, is found in large numbers. It has white spots like little stars along its body. It feeds mainly on crustaceans and grows to a length of 1.5 m (4½ ft). A similar species, *Mustelus canis* [20], is found in the western North Atlantic.

18

21

22

Lemon Sharks (*Negaprion brevirostris*) of the family **Carcharinidae,** are found along the coasts of South Carolina and Florida. Their jaws [21] have very large, sharp teeth, and the species is thought to be responsible for attacks on people bathing. Apart from this, however, the species is of some economic significance; the fins in particular are highly prized as a delicacy, and the liver has a high oil content. The **Blue Shark,** *Prionace glauca* [23], is an inhabitant of tropical and temperate seas. In summer it migrates into inshore European waters.

The extraordinary broadening of the head into the shape of a hammer with a resulting wide spacing of both nostrils and eyes makes the Hammer-

headed Sharks (family **Sphyrnidae**) of particular interest. They live in warm seas throughout the world. In the neighbourhood of Cuba particularly large numbers of *Sphyrna mokarran* [22] are found. These sharks provide man with valuable oils from the liver. Hammerheads generally seek their food on the sea bottom, but also eat surface-living fishes, and it is not unusual to see them following a ship in search of waste matter thrown overboard. Occasionally people swimming or working in the water have been attacked by them.

The family **Squalidae** contains species of sharks with a large spine in front of the dorsal fin. The most abundant species in European waters is

23

Squalus acanthias, the **Spur Dog**, but many other kinds are found in deep waters including the genus *Oxynotus*, which has been found chiefly in the eastern Atlantic, and in the Australian region.

Oxynotus centrina [24] lives in the Mediterranean and Atlantic. The species *Centrophorus granulosus* [25] is an example of a deep-sea shark: specimens have been caught off the coasts of Portugal at a depth of nearly 900 m (3,000 ft).

Several other species are known in deep water in the north Atlantic; all are deep chocolate brown in colour with shining green eyes. The young are found in shallower water than the adults, which rarely grow longer than 2 m (6 ft).

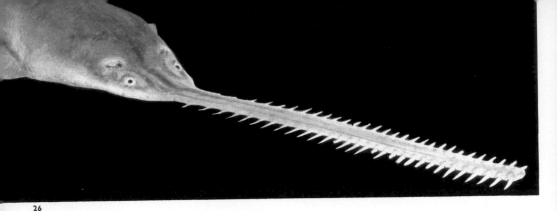

The second order of Elasmobranchs consists of the Rays **(Batoidei)**. Their body is flat, and they are mainly bottom-living. The eyes are dorsally placed, the mouth and gills are ventral; the pectoral fins are well developed and fused with the body in front.

Many stories are told of the Sawfishes (family **Pristidae**), which sometimes use their 'saw' to defend themselves against enemies. This saw consists of an elongated snout with teeth along each side. Sawfishes keep to the bottom, digging with their saw into the sand and mud for their food. Although they are not aggressive, they are capable of dealing a fatal wound to man with their

powerful bodies. The **Common Sawfish,** *Pristis pectinatus* [26], has a comparatively large number of teeth on its saw — usually around twenty-four pairs. These Sawfishes grow to a length of 6 m (19 ft).

The Electric Rays, family **Torpedinidae** (suborder **Torpedinoidei**), have electric organs occupying the greater part of the bases of the pectoral fins. The **Marbled Electric Ray,** *Torpedo marmorata* [27], has a slightly rounded body with a marbled pattern on its back. The spiracles, which are situated behind the eyes, have several whitish papillae round the edge. The electric shocks produced by the organs may be a defence against aggressors,

27

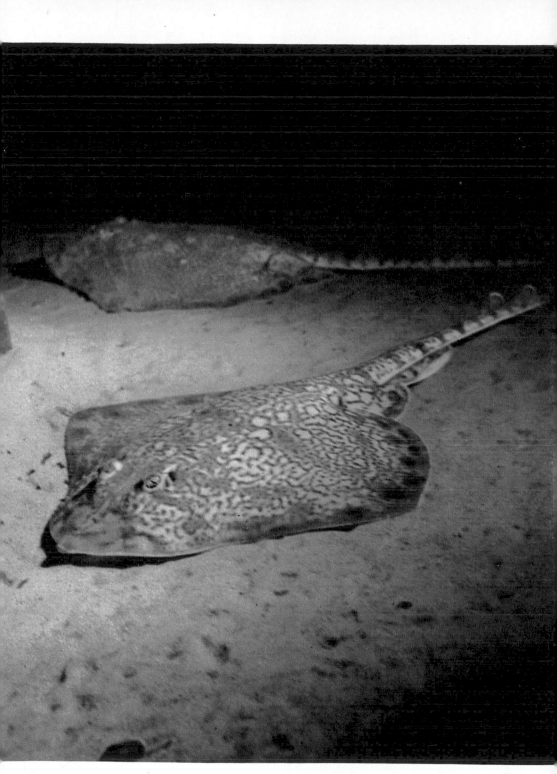

29

but they are primarily used to stun the often large and active fishes on which they feed. These organs are evolved from special muscles, and are kidney-shaped. The individual muscle fibres have been transformed into electrical elements, which lie in vast numbers in vertical, hexagonal, jelly-filled tubes. The current emitted by a single element is of course tiny, but together they can produce a shock of some 300 volts at an intensity of 7–8 amperes in some of the larger species. About thirty species of Electric Ray are known in tropical and temperate seas, of which the largest is the Atlantic *Torpedo nobiliana*. They all give birth to live young.

The family **Rajidae** (suborder **Rajoidei**) contains the Skates and smaller Rays. All of them have spines down the middle of their back and tail. The tail is long and narrow, and the tail fin is very small. The **Thornback Ray**, *Raja clavata* [28], is very common in European coastal waters, and has particularly well developed spines on its skin. In common with all other Rays its eggs have a protective casing [29]. The egg case has a horn at each corner, and is up to 11 cm (4 in) long. The young Rays which emerge from it are practically identical to the adults. Rays are always white underneath, although the back varies greatly in colour. The mouth, nostrils and gill slits can be seen in picture 30. As in the case of the Sharks, the

30

male Rays have paired copulatory organs (*mixopterygia*), which are modified from the pelvic fins.

The Stingray family (**Dasyatidae**, suborder **Myliobatoidea**) contains many brightly coloured species, for example *Taeniura lymna* [31], which has a brown back with blue spots and is sometimes kept in captivity in aquaria. Stingrays are very widely distributed throughout tropical and temperate seas. *Dasyatis violacea* [32] and *Dasyatis*

31

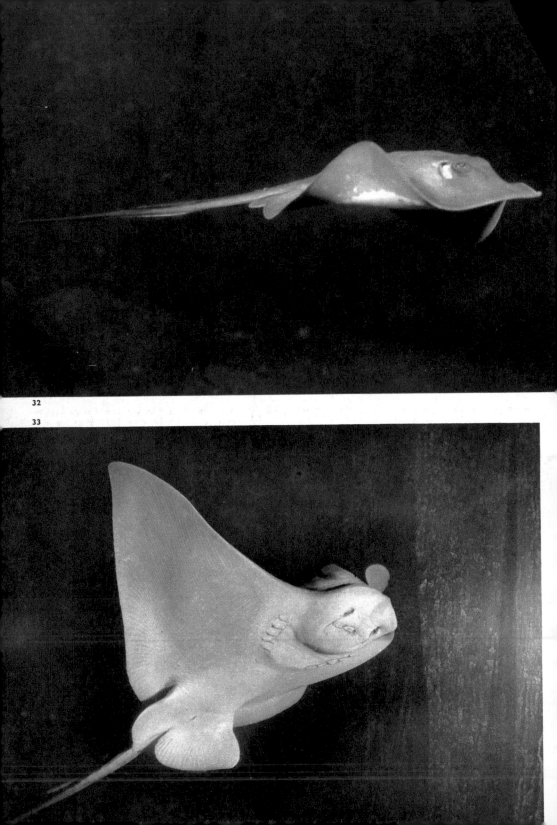

32

33

1   American Bowfin *(Amia calva)*

2a Brown Trout *(Salmo trutta* morpha *fario)*
2b Brook Charr *(Salvelinus fontinalis)*

pastinaca are found in the Mediterranean, the latter also on the British coast. Other members of the family Dasyatidae inhabit equatorial seas, while some live in the Plate, Marañon, and Senegal rivers.

One of the best-known members of the family **Urolophidae** is *Urolophus jamaicensis*, the **Jamaican Stingray** [35], which is very common throughout the Caribbean and neighbouring waters. It is distinguished by a well-developed tail fin. The back of this ray bears an attractive pattern of dark green waves and spots, often with white, yellow, or golden markings on a darker ground; the variations in colouring are enormous. It lives mainly in sand- and mudbanks, and feeds on worms, shellfish, and on small fishes. Like most of the Stingrays, it has poison glands at the base of the tail spine, and can inflict severe injuries with the spine and its venom.

Rays of the family **Myliobatidae** are distributed throughout the oceans of the world, except in the coldest parts. They grow to a length of something over 1 m (3 ft). The **Eagle Ray,** *Myliobatis aquila* [33], is present in the Mediterranean and eastern Atlantic, northwards to southern Norway, and is also found in the Indian Ocean along the coasts

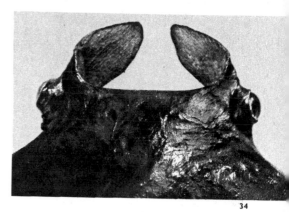

34

of South Africa. Its method of swimming is most impressive and extremely fast. Sometimes it leaps clear of the surface of the water. The Eagle Ray has flat, crushing teeth set in powerful jaws with which it can crush even large, heavy-shelled clams. It is often a pest to shellfish fishermen.

The largest Rays belong to the Devil Ray family **(Mobulidae).** These live in tropical seas and are particularly numerous on the coasts of tropical

35

36

America. The **Atlantic Manta (***Manta birostris***)**
has immensely broad fins, almost wing-like in
shape, and a pair of horn-like projections at the
front of its head [34]. With pectoral fins fully
extended it has a total span of some 7 m (23 ft).
It weighs anything up to 1,000 kg (1 ton). It is
ovoviviparous, and the young are born weighing
around 10 kg (22 lb). It feeds on small planktonic
creatures, chiefly crustaceans and small fishes, and
it is frequently seen near the surface of the water,
either alone or in pairs.

Members of the class Holocephali (Rabbitfishes and
Chimaeras) are first found as early as the Lower
Cretaceous, and during the Permian became distinct
from the primitive Sharks of the subclass Clado-
selachii which were ancestral to many later types.

38

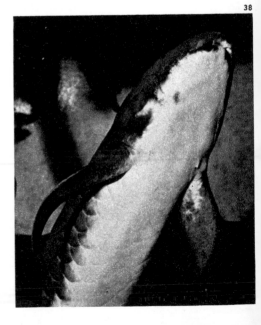

37

39

In common with the Selachians they have a distinctive egg case, and share the same fundamental anatomical structure: the males also possess claspers. Only a few genera of this ancient and once abundant class have survived down to the present

40

day, and of these the most familiar species is the **Rabbitfish,** *Chimaera monstrosa* [36], an inhabitant of the Mediterranean and the Atlantic Ocean. It grows to a length of about 1 m (3 ft). It lives in deep waters where it feeds on molluscs, crustaceans and starfishes on the bottom. It is rarely found at less than 100 m (330 ft), and is most common on the continental shelf.

The Lungfishes (class Dipnoi) show traces of a relationship both with the primitive selachians and with highly modified amphibians. The notochord

41

persists throughout the creature's life; there are no bony vertebral centres. The gill openings are covered by a gill cover. The swim-bladder, which opens ventrally to the gullet, has one or two lobes and a distinctive, lung-like circulatory system. The atrium of the heart is imperfectly divided into left and right chambers. The **Australian Lung-fish**, *Neoceratodus forsteri* [37], a member of the order **Ceratodiformes**, lives in marshy waters in north-east Australia. In many ways this is the most primitive of the Lungfishes. It has large scales, flipper-like pelvic and pectoral fins, and only one lung. Unlike the other Lungfishes it does not aestivate in a mud tube or ball, and in well-oxygen-

ated water it seems to obtain all the oxygen it needs through its gills as it does not gulp at the surface. The Australian Lungfish is confined to a relatively small area in the Burnett and Mary rivers but is now closely protected. The creature grows to a length of 150 cm (60 in) and weighs 10 kg (22 lb). When fully grown it feeds on worms, molluscs and small fishes.

The genus *Protopterus* (family **Protopteridae**, order **Lepidosireniformes**), comes from Africa. Its members are furnished with a pair of lung-sacs. At the beginning of the dry season they prepare for aestivation, digging a sloping shaft between

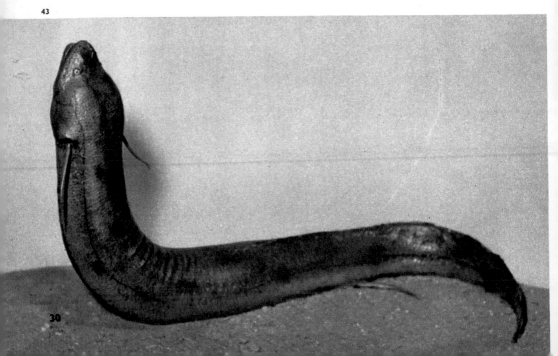

50–77 cm (20–32 in) long in the mud of the river bottom. At the foot of this shaft they build a cocoon of mud, dead vegetation, and slime, which protects them against the danger of becoming dehydrated. Within the cocoon the Lungfish lies head upwards with its tail over its eyes. Only a tiny hole to breathe through connects it with the outside world. When the rainy season comes the sun-baked outside walls of the capsule are softened and the fish is set free.

The **African Lungfish**, *Protopterus dolloi* [39], is an outstanding example of considerable variation in colouring among specimens of the same species. The paired pectoral and pelvic fins are threadlike. The branched sensory lines along the sides of the head are quite striking [41]. The adult African Lungfish is about 2 m (6 ft) in length. It obtains oxygen partly by using its gills, partly by breathing through its lungs. In [40] it is taking a deep breath at the surface of the water. One of the most impressively coloured Lungfishes is the **East African Lungfish**, *Protopterus aethiopicus* [42]. The larvae which hatch from the eggs possess four pairs of feathery external gills. The male protects both the spawn and the young fishes.

45

46

47

32

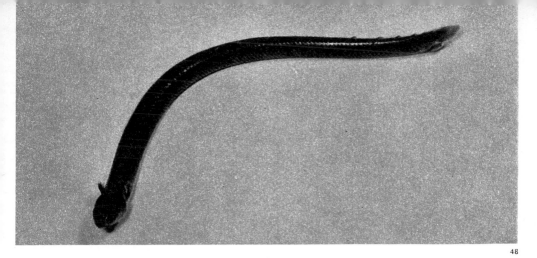

The **South American Lungfish,** *Lepidosiren paradoxa* [43], lives in muddy waters in the Amazon basin and the Gran Chaco. It reaches a length of 1 m (3 ft). In the dry season it breathes exclusively through its lungs and does not feed but lives off the fat accumulated during the preceding rainy season. Like the African Lungfishes it has a double lung.

The largest class of fishes is the Teleostomi, or Bony Fishes. The first subclass is that of the Lobe-finned Fishes (Crossopterygii). Most members of this subclass are now extinct, and today only the genus *Latimeria* [44] belonging to the order **Coelacanthiformes** (hollow-spined fishes) has survived. The first modern Coelacanth was caught in 1938 off the south-east coast of Africa at a depth of about 72 m (240 ft). This catch caused a considerable stir, for related forms were up till then only known from palaeontological discoveries. Fourteen years later, in 1952, a second specimen was caught in the vicinity of the Comoro Islands, north-west of Madagascar. Since then further specimens have been caught from time to time. French ichthyologists in particular have made detailed studies of the creature's anatomy.

Another subclass whose members are distinguished by an archaic bone structure is that of the Ray-finned Fishes (Actinopterygii), containing the order of Bichirs or Lobe-fins **(Polypteriformes).** A number of remarkable characteristics connects these with the extinct Crossopterygians. Fossil Lobe-fins are known from Eocene remains in Egypt. The reconstruction proposed on the basis of the large scales which have been found give the extinct species a length of some 180 cm (6 ft). Today only one family of Lobe-fins survives, the **Polypteridae.** About ten species are recognized in the genus *Polypterus.* Two brightly coloured species from the Congo are *Polypterus delhezi* [45] and *Polypterus ornatipinnis* [46]. A comparatively small species, *Polypterus palmas* [47], lives in the rivers of Guinea, Liberia, and the Congo. This achieves a length of only 30–35 cm (12–14 in). Its nasal openings are extended into what look like projecting tubes [49]. It is often imported by aquarists, and can be bred successfully. It is a nocturnal predator. The **Reedfish,** *Calamoichthys calabricus* [48], which is the sole representative of the genus *Calamoichthys*, lives in the Niger delta. The long, eel-like body of this species is characterized by the absence of pelvic fins and by well-separated dorsal finlets. Its greatest length amounts to 90 cm (36 in).

The great majority of Sturgeons, subclass Chondrostei, belong to the order **Acipenseriformes**. The body is covered with five rows of bony scutes (large, shield-like scales). The upper part of the tail fin is somewhat extended. The most numerous species belong to the genus *Acipenser* (family **Acipenseridae**). The **Sterlet**, *Acipenser ruthenus* [50], lives throughout the year in fresh water; only in the northern tributaries of the Caspian Sea can it be found in brackish water. It swims as far up the Danube as Bavaria. It grows to a length of only 50 cm (20 in). Sterlets are highly prized, and in the Soviet Union about 60 tons are caught each year. The mouth, which has four barbels in

52

51

front [51], can be shot out to form a funnel or tube, through which it sucks up its food from the bottom. This consists primarily of worms and molluscs.

The **Common Sturgeon**, *Acipenser sturio* [53], is found in European waters and along the North American coast from Hudson Bay to South Carolina. It grows to a length of 3 m (6 ft) and achieves a weight of up to 200 kg (440 lb). It lays its eggs in rivers and after a short period in fresh water the young fishes migrate to the sea. In consequence the Sturgeon is most often seen as a sea fish. Breeding stocks have become small in European waters and today it is a relatively rare fish.

Acipenser guldenstadti lives in the rivers which flow into the Black Sea, the Sea of Azov and the Caspian. This fish migrates up river, and grows to a length of 2.5 m (8 ft). Two races are distinguished, the autumn and spring varieties, so called on account of the season in which they undertake their migration. This is the largest Sturgeon caught in the Soviet Union. The Black Sea and the Sea of Azov populations are referred to a subspecies, *Acipenser guldenstadti colchicus* [52], of which specimens weighing over 50 kg (110 lb) and more than 2 m (6 ft) in length have been caught in the Dnieper. It is very common on the coasts around the Caucasus, but is rarer along the Bulgarian coast. The migration of this Sturgeon up the river Don from the Sea of Azov begins in March and reaches its greatest height in April and May. During the migratory period the female may have nearly double the weight of a male of the same size.

54

Acipenser nudiventris [54] comes from the Aral-Caspian area. During the last 100 years it has found its way into the Danube and has got as far as Budapest. Its spawning season is from March to May. Not all the newly hatched fishes travel down to the sea immediately: some of them remain for over a year in the river. Spawning takes place at two to three year intervals.

The **Beluga,** *Huso huso* [55], is distinguished by its short, round snout, flat barbels, and a large, semicircular mouth. This species is also distributed in the Aral-Caspian area. It grows to a length of 9 m (25 ft), can weigh up to 1,500 kg (3,300 lb), and can live for more than 100 years. Specimens found in the Volga are usually autumn migrators, whereas in the river Ural both autumn and spring races are found. In youth the Beluga feeds principally on invertebrates but the adult feeds on larger organisms including fishes. Young Caspian Seals have even been found in the stomachs of the larger specimens. This fish is of enormous economic importance because its black eggs (the roe) provide valuable caviar.

56

The genus *Scaphirhynchus* consists of Sturgeons with a dorsoventrally flattened head and an elongated tail. The **Shovelnose Sturgeon,** *Scaphirhynchus platorhynchus* [56], is found in fresh water from Hudson Bay to Arkansas. When fully grown it is 90 cm (3 ft) long and weighs 3 kg (6½ lb); it feeds on small bottom-living creatures such as snails, crayfishes, insect larvae and small fishes.

Certain species of the genus *Pseudoscaphirhynchus* are distinguished by a spade-shaped snout. The **Shovelfish,** *Pseudoscaphirhynchus kaufmanni* [58], comes from the river Amu-Darya and grows to a length of 75 cm (32 in). It spawns in spring. The immature fish feeds on insect larvae, while the adult specimens eat fishes, principally Loaches. The

tail is continued into an unusually long threadlike process [57]. On the upper side of the snout there are between one and five bizarre-looking thorns [59]. In larger specimens the thorns in front of the eyes disappear and only those behind the eyes remain.

Another spoonbilled Sturgeon, the **Paddlefish,** *Polyodon spathula* [60], which is a member of the family **Polyodontidae,** is found in the Mississippi basin. This reaches a length of 2 m (6 ft) and a weight of 90 kg (200 lb). It differs from other Sturgeons in several ways, notably in the formation of its mouth which can be opened widely. It feeds on planktonic animals, which it filters out of the water with its long gill rakers on the inside of its throat.

57

58

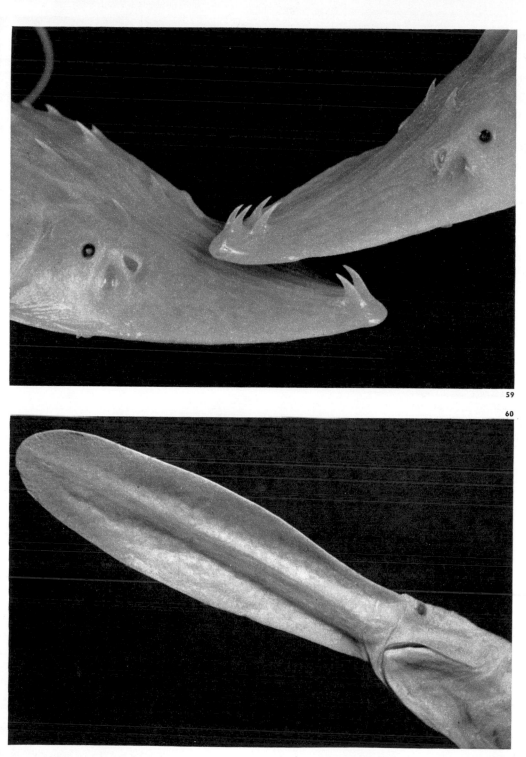

At the beginning of this century the Paddlefish was of some economic significance, the annual catch amounting to about 1,000 tons. Its roe in particular was valuable. However, as a result of pollution of the rivers and the erection of dams the yield has now sunk so low as to be negligible.

The order **Amiiformes** contains a number of extinct families. At the present day only one monotypic genus, *Amia*, has survived in the family **Amiidae.** This is represented by the **American Bowfin,** *Amia calva* [61, Pl. 1]. It inhabits North American rivers – the river systems of the Great Lakes (with the exception of Lake Superior) and the basin of the Mississippi. It is most common in well-weeded rivers and the margins of lakes. It grows to a length of 60 cm (24 in) and weighs 5 kg (11 lb). The male bears a striking dark, yellow-

ringed spot at the base of his tail. The Bowfin is mainly nocturnal, and the adult preys on small fishes. It spawns between May and June. A single spawning will give rise to some 64,000 eggs. The fry attach themselves to the nest with a little suction cup situated near the mouth. The nest and the fry are cared for by the male.

The **Lepisosteiformes** (Gar Pikes), represented by only one family, the **Lepisosteidae,** form another very ancient order. The genus *Lepisosteus* is known to have lived in the seas of Europe, North America, and India. Today, however, its members can only be encountered in North American waters as far south as Mexico and Cuba. The **Longnose Gar,** *Lepisosteus osseus* [62], grows to a length of some 150 cm (5 ft). It lives in the Great Lakes region and the Mississippi basin and

64

65

has a very long snout. The smallest species, the **Shortnose Gar,** *Lepisosteus platostomus* [63], is principally found in the region of the Great Lakes. This fish is·no more than 60 cm (2 ft) long. The largest species – the **Alligator Gar,** *Lepisosteus tristoechus* [64] – lives in coastal fresh and salt water in the areas surrounding the Caribbean. It grows to a length of 3 m (10 ft) and a weight of 75 kg (65 lb). Nevertheless it grows very slowly. It can survive in ox-bow lakes during the dry season in very small quantities of water, and is usually found in shallow weedy areas. Most of the time they hang motionless in the water, ready to make a lightning charge at passing fishes. It is not sought after as food because of its large number of bones. The body is covered in strong ganoid scales arranged in diamond shaped plates. The long jaws have numerous teeth. The swim-bladder serves as an auxiliary breathing organ. An Alligator Gar, some 50 cm (20 in) long, is shown [65] swallowing a Veil-tail Goldfish.

3   Angling for Grayling

4 A Grayling in the net

The vast majority of fishes living today belong to the subclass of modern bony fishes, Teleostei. The order **Clupeiformes** contains several suborders. Today some fifty genera with approximately 160 species are recognized. The suborder **Clupeoidei** contains a number of families and species which are of great economic significance. The most familiar is the **Herring,** *Clupea harengus* [66], which is distributed in the North Atlantic and as a subspecies in the Pacific. The annual catch of Herrings throughout the world amounts to 6,000,000 tons, representing about thirty-seven per cent of the total yield of fishes throughout the world. Herrings are pelagic fishes. Relatives are the Sardines, and the Anchovies, European members of which belong to the genera *Sardina* and *Engraulis*. In the spawning season they congregate in huge schools.

The suborder **Phractolaemoidei** (African Mud-

67

fishes) is characterized by a small head and a protrusible, toothless mouth. The genus *Phractolaemus* inhabits fresh water in tropical western Africa – principally the Niger and Congo deltas. The only known species, *Phractolaemus ansorgei* [67], grows to a length of 15 cm (6 in) and it is occasionally kept in aquaria. In the natural state it inhabits muddy water and feeds on minute animals in the mud. It requires a temperature of 25–28°C.

The suborder **Salmonoidei** (Salmons) is characterized by the presence of an adipose dorsal fin just in front of the tail. It embraces twelve families, including one which is now extinct. The oviduct of the female is incomplete or entirely absent; the ripe eggs pass freely from the ovaries into the body cavity and are expressed through the genital opening during spawning. Members of this suborder are present in both the northern and southern hemispheres, and are found in both fresh water and the sea.

The best-known member of the family **Salmonidae** is the **Salmon**, *Salmo salar* [71], which inhabits the

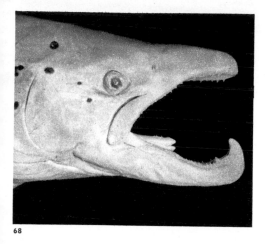

north Atlantic Ocean. These fishes are anadromous and grow to a length of 1.5 m (5 ft) and weigh up to 38 kg (84 lb). They swim up river to spawn, but spend the greater part of their life in the open sea. Before spawning the jaws of the male change shape: the upper jaw develops a knob at its end and the lower jaw becomes hooked [68].

The **Sea Trout**, *Salmo trutta*, is found in north-western Europe and spawns in fresh water. It is probably close to the ancestral form which gave rise to the **Brown Trout**, *Salmo trutta* morpha *fario* [70, Pl. 2a)]. Both forms spawn in late autumn. The Brown Trout has distinctive red spots, although this is not true of every individual: those which

71

live in lakes and reservoirs tend to lose their red colouring.

Large mature males often have hook-shaped lower jaws. The mouth of the female [69] differs greatly

in shape and size from that of the male fish. Brown Trout are favourite fishes for anglers and can be caught in mountain streams or at the foot of water-falls [72]. They may sometimes be seen leaping at the water's surface [74]. Trout can be taken in

73

74

75

a number of ways, but fly-fishing is particularly successful [76].

Occasionally a fish weighing as much as 2.5 kg (5½ lb) may be caught [73]. The last phase of a successful catch consists of bringing the exhausted fish to land with a net [75]. Since most rivers and streams are dammed and many of them are consid-

erably polluted, artificial hatching is now very important. For hatchery purposes Trout are caught with the aid of an electrical fish stunner and net. The landing net is connected to an anode. When the current is switched on the fish are stunned and can then be brought in with the landing net quite successfully. Fishes being caught under a weir are shown [77]. An experienced angler makes use of an

electric shock to force the fishes to swim out of their hiding place and into the landing net. A Grayling is shown swimming into the landing net [78].

Another valuable fish, originally from north-west America, is the **Rainbow Trout**, *Salmo gairdneri*

[79]. This Trout has been bred in Europe for more than sixty years. In Europe it spawns only in spring, although in its native surroundings autumn spawning varieties are also found. Although widely stocked for angling in the British Isles it rarely establishes itself as a breeding population. It grows more

80

quickly in fish ponds than the Brown Trout and
will also take a greater variety of food. Members
of the genus *Oncorhynchus* live in the basin of the
North Pacific, spawning in fresh water. The species
Oncorhynchus tschawytscha comes from the Yukon

in Alaska and grows to a length of 1.5 m (5 ft)
and a weight of 45 kg (100 lb).

The genus *Hucho* occurs in river systems across
Europe and Asia from the Danube to Korea. The

Huchen, *Hucho hucho,* lives in the Danube basin and is also found in the Dniester. It is up to 1.5 m (5 ft) long and weighs up to 53 kg (117 lb). A typical Huchen river is the Orava in Slovakia [80], where angling for large fishes amongst the ice floes can be particularly exciting sport. However, women can also catch Huchen successfully [81]. This particular catch weighed 8 kg (18 lb). Unlike other members of the Salmon family, Huchen are generally brownish in colouring and have the

typically expressive eyes of predatory fishes [82]. In recent years the Huchen has become a rather rare fish in many of its natural haunts. For this reason this species too is being bred artificially. Large specimens are selected and prepared for artificial spawning by being laid for a few minutes on a linen sheet [83] to pacify them.

Then the hatchery-keeper strokes the sides of the fish's body, pressing the roe out through the genital pore into a basin [84]. The milters are handled in exactly same way. After the semen has been mixed with the roe the fertilized eggs are washed

82

83

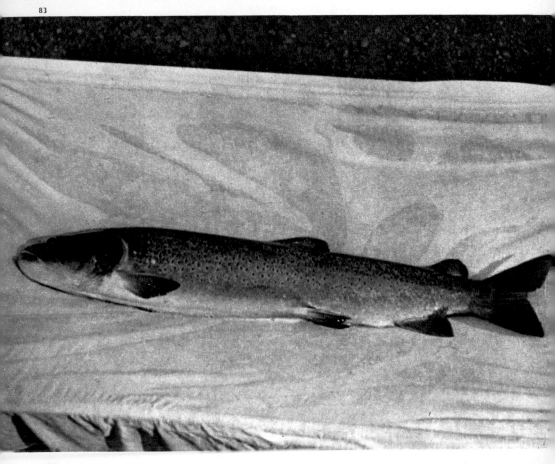

and placed in hatching troughs [85], which have a constant flow of oxygenated fresh water. The period of development of both Huchen and Trout eggs depends on the temperature of the water, although it is different in each species. At first the larva has a large external yolk sac on which it feeds. If the young fishes are moved before the yolk is absorbed considerable losses may be expected. They are kept in the troughs until the young fishes are able to feed independently [86], then they are put out into fish ponds. As a rule the fishes are put into streams and larger lakes when they are yearlings.

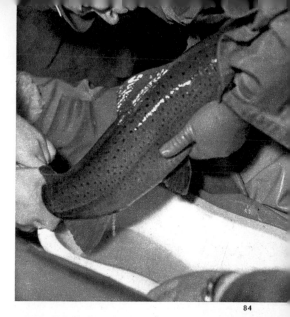

84

85

86

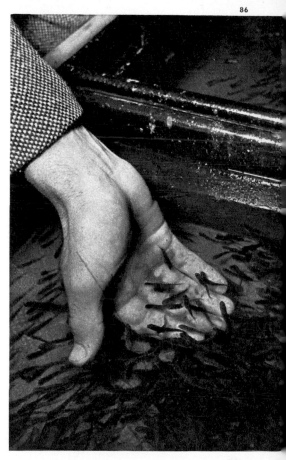

The members of the genus *Salvelinus* are migratory fishes found in rivers flowing into the Arctic Ocean, but they are also found in non-migratory form in mountain lakes in the British Isles and Europe. The **Brook Trout,** *Salvelinus fontinalis* [87, Pl. 2b], is a native of the cold waters of Labrador, although it is found as far south as Georgia. It grows to

a length of 1 m (3 ft) and a weight of 7.5 kg (17 lb). At the end of the last century it was introduced to central Europe, and has been released in British rivers.

The genus *Coregonus* is characterized by a narrow body, large scales, and toothless jaws. A familiar

species is the **Houting** or **Powan,** *Coregonus lavaretus* [88], which in Europe is often kept in artificial fish pools, and in the British Isles is found in a few mountain lakes.

It feeds on plankton, and when 130 cm (52 in) long can be expected to weigh 10 kg (22 lb). Between the mountain streams inhabited by the Brown Trout and the more placid waters of the Barbel lie the reaches where the Grayling is found. Angling for **Grayling** [Pl. 3] is also quite an art for the

fishes are wary and in order to catch them with the fly considerable experience and patience are required. However, in the end there is no escape from the angler's net [Pl. 4]. Even out of the water the Grayling, *Thymallus thymallus* [Pl. 5], retain their shimmering rainbow colouring for a time. The form *Thymallus thymallus lacustris* [89] is found in large lakes, while *Thymallus arcticus baicalensis* [90] comes from Lake Baikal. All these forms are of economic importance in central Europe.

5 A pair of Grayling

6   Pike *(Esox lucius)*

The Pike group, suborder **Esocoidei**, is distinguished by having the pelvic fins in the middle of
the body. In contrast to the Salmonoidei they do
not have an adipose fin, and their fins lack spines.
The European **Mudminnow**, *Umbra krameri* [91],
belongs to the family **Umbridae** and lives in the
river systems of the Danube and the Dniester. It
grows to a length of about 10 cm (4 in) and keeps to
overgrown backwaters and even semi-swamps.
The **Pike**, *Esox lucius* [92], of the family **Esocidae**,

is distributed throughout northern Europe, northern Asia, and North America. It prefers still or gently flowing waters with plentiful plant growth. Pike may grow to a length of 1.5 m (5 ft) and a weight of 65 kg (143 lb) but it is unusual for a catch to weigh more than 10 kg (22 lb). The Pike's method of dealing with its prey may be observed in an aquarium. The victim is seized by the head [93] and then simply swallowed whole [94]. In nature the Pike feeds chiefly on fishes and mostly on members of the Carp group but it will also attack other water creatures, such as small mammals, young birds and amphibians. Normally the Pike does little damage in Bream waters; it is a very different case, however, if it happens to stray into Trout or Grayling territory. Its behaviour towards other members of its own species is very interesting. Each large individual takes possession of and defends its own territory. When the area becomes crowded the Pike fight among themselves, and the weaker members are eaten by the larger ones. Trolling for Pike with a spoon will always afford good sport. One Pike which was caught in the Lipno Reservoir in the Bohemian Forest and was reeled in to the muddy bank is shown in colour plate 6. Its flecked, grey-green colouring gives it complete camouflage in its natural surroundings and enables it to lie in wait for its prey unnoticed. Pike spawn in flooded meadows in early spring.

95

96

97

To provide sufficient Pike for sport fishing and to keep a healthy balance between prey and predators in rivers it has become necessary to breed and raise Pike artificially in the same way as Trout. In picture 95 the milt is being added to the eggs; both are stirred together with a goose quill while fresh water is run over them. The fertilized eggs are then put into special flasks [96]. Picture 97 shows eggs which have reached what is called the eyed stage, when the dark colouring matter has already formed in the pigmentation cells of the spawn. Young Pike hatch with a large yolk sac [98] which they quickly absorb and begin to feed independently.

99

While still using their yolk reserves the young fishes are ladled out into their natural habitat [99], where they find ample food to support themselves. In putting the young fishes out it is important to space the groups in order to prevent cannibalism to which the Pike is inclined from an early age. The fry grow quickly.

The **Arapaima,** *Arapaima gigas* [100], is a member of the family **Arapaimidae** and the suborder **Osteoglossoidei** (Bony Tongues). It lives in the tropical waters of South America and grows to a length of 3 m (10 ft) with a weight of 200 kg (440 lb). It is the largest fresh-water fish in the world. Another Bony Tongue is the **Arawana,**

Osteoglossum bicirrhosum [101], which lives in the northern part of South America, in Guyana and in the Amazon basin. It is often found in huge shoals in still water or in shallow backwaters and lakes. Its food ranges from plankton up to quite large fishes. Arawanas are known as mouthbrooders, for the female keeps the eggs in her mouth until the young fishes emerge. The two comparatively long barbels on the lower jaw [102] are a characteristic of this species.

100

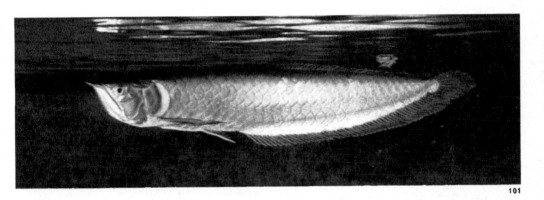

101

102

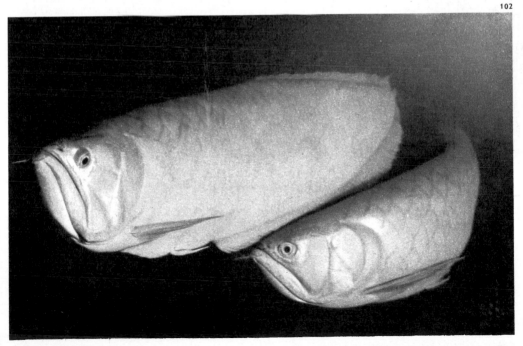

103

104

The **Butterfly Fish**, *Pantodon buchholzi* [103], a member of the suborder **Pantodontoidei**, bears large, wing-like pectoral fins. The abdominal fins are small, but extended into a number of long, threadlike rays. *Pantodon buchholzi* is a fresh-water fish, found In tropical Africa, particularly the area of the Niger and the Congo. It spends its time near the surface, for it leaps out to catch passing insects. Seen from above, it resembles a butterfly rather than a fish [104]. It is often kept in aquaria and, although difficult to rear, it has been bred in warm peaty water in captivity. It requires a large shallow tank at a temperature of 25–30°C, and prefers cockroaches, crickets, and such like as food. The Butterfly Fish is about 10 cm (4 in) long when fully grown.

The Nile and waters of tropical Africa are inhabited by members of the order **Mormyriformes**. Certain representatives of the genus *Gnathonemus*, family **Mormyridae**, are distinguished by a long, tube-like snout. These fishes are found portrayed on the walls of Egyptian temples. The **Elephant-trunk Mormyrid**, *Gnathonemus elephas* [105], comes from the upper Niger. It reaches a length of 40 cm (16 in), is dark brown to violet in colour

and prefers dark places. In aquaria it is a placid fish, and is not difficult to keep.

The order **Cypriniformes** (Carps) consists of fresh-water fishes which are distinguished by a row of small bones, known as the Weberian apparatus, which connects the inner ear with the swim-bladder. Members of the Cypriniformes are found as early as the Upper Cretaceous.

The most primitive suborder is that of the Characins **(Characinoidei)**. The family **Characidae** contains a very large number of members distributed from the Rio Grande southwards throughout Central and South America. They are also found throughout Africa except in the far south. Several hundred species are popular throughout the world as aquarium fishes.

The **Humpbacked Headstander**, *Characinus gibbosus* [106], lives in Guyana, in the central parts of the Amazon, and in the river Paraguay. It generally swims at an angle, with its head down. Its body is greyish-yellow and transparent so that the intestines and skeletal structure are clearly visible. It feeds principally on living animal matter.

106

107

The Piranha group consists of several much-feared species of fresh-water fishes from South America. The best known of them are vicious predators, with a length of some 35 cm (14 in), such as the **Black Piranha**, *Serrasalmus niger* [107], or the **Piraya**, *Pygocentrus piraya* [109, Pl. 7], which are found in Guyana and the Amazon basin. They attack in large shoals with such ferocity that even alligators are quickly overwhelmed and reduced to a skeleton by the Piranhas' sharp ripping teeth [108]. Bathing in Piranha-infested rivers is dangerous even for man. Fishermen dread them for they will grab fishes from the net. Their aggression, voracity, and fearlessness are incredible.

The smaller species, for example the **Silver Dollar Fish**, *Mylossoma argenteum* [110], feed on plants as well as on animals. In their native surroundings in the southern part of the Amazon basin and the upper Paraguay they reach a length of 20 cm (8 in). Some members of the genus *Metynnis* are almost exclusively herbivorous and consume surprisingly

108

109

110

large quantities of water plants. In aquaria they can be fed successfully on lettuce.

The export of plant-eating Characins from South America has been made illegal, since the enormous appetite of these fishes enables them to keep backwaters and creeks free from excessive plant growth, thus ensuring penetration of light through the water. Without light life is extinguished and the water putrefies.

111

Metynnis schreitmuelleri [111], is only 15 cm (6 in) in length. The species *Metynnis calichromus* [112], is a native of the Jamunda, the northern tributary of the central Amazon flowing through the city of Faro. It, too, grows to a length of 5 cm. The waters of northern South America contain the **Pacu,** *Colossoma nigripinnis* [113], which feeds principally on ripe fruit and grows to a length of some 70 cm (24 in). This species is more common in zoological gardens or in large public aquaria.

114

115

A popular aquarium fish is the **Bloodfin**, *Aphyocharax rubripinnis* [114], which is a native of Parana and the Argentine. Its maximum length is only about 5.5 cm (2 in). This undemanding, lively little fish does very well in aquaria which are in a sunny situation. The parent fishes lay their eggs on plants. The fry emerge after only thirty hours if the water temperature is between 24 and 28°C. The little fishes grow quickly and will feed equally well on living, dried, or artificially prepared food.

Moenkhausia pittieri comes from Venezuela. It grows to a length of 6 cm (2½ in). The male has elongated rays in the dorsal, tail, and pelvic fins [115]. This fish, with its silvery sheen and unusual liveliness, is a boon to any aquarium. It feeds principally on plankton and needs soft water. Its relative *Moenkhausia sanctaefilomenae* [Pl. 8a], grows to a length of 7 cm (3 in) and comes from the

Paraguay river system and the basin of the river Paranahiba. The upper part of its iris is red. At the roots of the tail it has a golden-yellow stripe crossing a black one. Its principal foodstuff consists of zooplankton.

The **Black Widow** or **Black Tetra**, *Gymnocorymbus ternetzi* [116], has a narrow flattened body. The adult male is always smaller than the female and its colouring is matt dark grey to black. This fish lives in the Matto Grosso region of the river Paraguay, and the Rio Negro and measures 5.5 cm (2 in) when grown. The fry swim in large shoals and make a unique impression: they all follow the same course with military precision and change direction together as if at a word of command. In recent years aquarists have succeeded in breeding a veiled form in which – particularly in the males – both the dorsal and pelvic fins as well as the forks of the tail fin are greatly lengthened.

117

118

7 Piraya *(Pygocentrus piraya)*

8a *Moenkhausia sanctae-filomenae*
8b *Petitella georgiae*

119

Another common aquarium species coming from the upper regions of the Amazon and the Marañon is the **Penguin Fish,** *Thayeria boehlkei* [117], which always swims at an angle with its head upwards. In aquaria they only spawn at twilight. The eggs are brownish in colouring and at a temperature of 26°C the fry emerge after only eighteen to twenty-four hours. Although these little fishes are only some 8 cm (3 in) long, they can, when kept in an uncovered tank or when being caught, leap some 1.5 –2 m (5–6 ft) out of the water. Less well known is *Thayeria obliqua* [118], also called the Penguin Fish, which comes from the lower waters of the Amazon. In this species the characteristic black stripe is only found on the very rear of the body, and the lower fork of the tail fin is larger and has a noticeably yellow edge.

The **X-ray Fish** or **Water Goldfinch,** *Pristella riddlei* [119], is a native of northern South America. It often reaches into brackish water. It grows to a length of 4.5 cm (2 in) and is easily bred in aquaria.

Central and South America have produced many gaily coloured species belonging to the genera *Hemigrammus* and *Hyphessobrycon* which in this century have achieved enormous popularity among aquarists. Generally they are small, colourful, and peaceable fishes. These, and related genera, are known collectively as Tetras. First of these is the **Buenos Aires Tetra,** *Hemigrammus caudovitatus* [120], which comes from the river Plate. The adult is almost exclusively vegetarian and about 7 cm (3 in) long. A shoal of these little fishes is able to root out completely the finest water plants in an

120

aquarium. With this exception, however, it is very easy to keep them: they have no difficulty in making themselves at home in properly prepared conditions.

121

The **Glow-light Tetra,** *Hemigrammus erythrozonus* [121], which comes from the waters of Guyana, grows to a length of 4.5 cm (2 in). This fish is very attractive with colourful, glittering stripes running the full length of the body. It lays eggs on tufts or small-leafed water plants (for example the aquatic moss *Fontinalis*). During spawning they carry out spiral movements, and the female generally takes up a position on her back. *Hemigrammus marginatus* [122], is distributed from Venezuela to the Argentine and grows to a length of 8 cm (3 in). It is difficult to breed in captivity. Spawning takes place at dawn just beneath the water's surface and the small, coffee-coloured to black eggs are attached irregularly to water plants; if the breeder does not take prompt action the parents will consume the eggs. This species is often confused with the **Red** or **Rummy-nosed Tetra,** *Hemigrammus rhodostomus*, which comes from the lower course of the Amazon and grows to a length of 5 cm (2 in). Its body shape and colouring is similar to that of the newly introduced *Petitella georgiae* [Pl. 8b]. The **Silver-tipped Tetra,** *Hemigrammus nanus* [123], is a little-known species from the San Francisco river system. It is generally less than 5 cm (2 in) in length, and its unremarkable colouring does not make it particularly popular with aquarists.

A more familiar species is the **Head-and-tail-light Fish** or **Beaconfish,** *Hemigrammus ocellifer ocellifer* [124], from the Amazon basin and from Guyana, which was discovered by Steindachner as

early as the year 1883. However, this form has only been kept successfully in aquaria since about 1958. The form *Hemigrammus ocellifer falsus* [125], which differs slightly from the specimens described by Steindachner, was described by Meinken in 1958. It is noticeably more slender, and has been successfully kept by aquarists since the beginning of this century.

The central waters of the Amazon are inhabited by the **Pretty Tetra,** *Hemigrammus pulcher* [126], which is about 6 cm (2½ in) long. It needs to be kept in soft, lightly oxygenated water at a temperature of 26°C. For successful spawning a large glass tank is necessary, for in small home aquaria the males are very aggressive and likely to hunt and kill the females before the eggs are fully ripe.

The **Feather Fin,** *Hemigrammus unilineatus* [127], is comparatively rare in aquaria. It comes from the waters of Trinidad and South America, where it reaches a length of 5 cm (2 in). The male is more slender and sometimes paler than the female.

The **Green Neon Tetra,** *Hemigrammus hyanuary* [128], enjoyed great popularity among aquarists after its introduction to Europe in 1955. It comes from the Amazon area and the adult is 4 cm (1½ in) long. Its basic colouring is olive-green with a whitish

belly. Along the sides of the upper half of the body there is a glittering, gold-green stripe. A large tank with soft water is necessary for successful breeding. It is comparatively shy and does not like abrupt changes in light.

Several subspecies of **Jewel Tetras,** *Hyphessobrycon callistus*, originating from the central Amazon and from north Paraguay, have been kept in aquaria for many years. These fishes grow to a length of 4.5 cm (2 in). *Hyphessobrycon callistus* [129] is

127

principally brick-red in colouring. Older specimens tend to be somewhat anti-social and bite off the fins of other Tetras kept with them. The most beautiful and lightest blood-red colouring is found in the **Serpae Tetra**, *Hyphessobrycon callistus serpae* [Pl. 9], which has a small black mark behind the gills. In aquaria it does not live to a great age, for it is subject to a large number of diseases. Nevertheless it reproduces readily.

By contrast the **Pink Jewelled Tetra**, *Hyphessobrycon callistus rosaceus* [130], is resilient and can be kept for years. It comes from the Essequibo in Guyana and reaches a length of 4 cm (1½ in). It needs soft water, slightly acidified by passing through peat. It lays its coffee-coloured eggs on the leaves of finely divided plants. For a few years now a similar subspecies imported from the USA, known under the trade description *Hyphessobrycon 'robertsi'* [Pl. 10], has been widely kept. It is larger than the Pink Jewelled Tetra and is differentiated from it principally by the colouring and the shape of its dorsal and pelvic fins. It is very difficult to keep. Nothing more is known at present about the origin of this fish.

128

131

One of the most widespread and sturdy Characins is the **Yellow Tetra**, *Hyphessobrycon bifasciatus* [131]. It is a native of coastal areas of south-east Brazil and grows to a length of up to 5 cm (2 in). The yellow-grey colouring of the adult is not particularly striking, but the fry of the Yellow Tetra have long red fins, and bear a striking resemblance to the **Bloodfin**, *Aphyocharax rubripinnis*. Not until it has lost its youthful colouring does this fish don the dull grey mantle of its parents. They are prolific breeders, and feed mainly on plants. although they will not refuse animal matter. A closely related species is the **Flame Tetra** or 'Red Tetra from Rio', *Hyphessobrycon flammeus* [132], which lives in the neighbourhood of Rio de Janeiro and is only some 4 cm (1½ in) long. The Flame Tetra is also very fertile and is cultivated by aquarists throughout the world since it is easy to keep. It is shown as spawning begins [133]. A further phase in spawning [134] is shown when the transparent, adhesive eggs attach themselves to plants. After spawning the parents must be removed from the tank, since like all Characins they will consume the eggs and later the young fry. Picture 135 shows a pair of adult Flame Tetras with their young: once the young have grown to this size they can be safely left in the same water as their parents. *Hyphessobrycon georgettae* [136], is a very

133

134

89

small species which was first described in 1961 by the French ichthyologist Géry. This little fish, only 2–3 cm (1 in) long, is interesting in that the eggs are comparatively large and the young fry have little difficulty in consuming quite large particles of food, for example the nauplii of *Cyclops* or the Brine Shrimp (*Artemia salina*). At the age of four to five months they are already full grown. *Hyphessobrycon gracilis* [137] comes from Guyana and Paraguay. It grows to a length of 4.5 cm (2 in) and was for a long time confused with *Hemigrammus erythrozonus*. As far as is known it has not been successfully bred in captivity. The species *Hyphessobrycon bellotti* [138] is likewise relatively rare. *Hyphessobrycon griemi* [139] is a native of the waters of Goyaz in Brazil. This, too, is a recent discovery and was described in 1957 by the Dutch ichthyologist Hoedeman. This fish is about 3 cm (1½ in) long and can be distinguished by its bright, rainbow

colouring. It is kept in much the same way as the Flame Tetra although it needs very soft water for spawning. In 1961, a new species of Tetra from Coxim on the river Taquary, *Hyphessobrycon herbertaxelrodi* [140], was made known. This is commonly called the **Black Neon Tetra** by aquarists, although from a systematic point of view this fish has nothing in common with the Neon Tetras. The length of this species is about 3–3.5 cm (1½ in) and it was welcomed among aquarists as a fine and beautiful new discovery. Its basic colouring is a light grey-green. On both sides of the body there is a dark grey or black band on which is an ivory-coloured strip along the upper edge. The young fishes grow to adulthood in a remarkably short time.

A very common species from South America, although its exact home is not known, is the

136

137

Lemon Tetra, *Hyphessobrycon pulchripinnis,* which grows to a length of some 5 cm (2 in). The colouring of this fish is made up of contrasting blacks and yellows, especially on the fins. Picture 141 shows a male with two females. Although Characins take no care for the rearing of their young the courtship play is of some interest. The male holds the female over a tangle of fine-leafed water plants, bending his body and trembling. After spawning both fishes swim away immediately.

In 1956 Hoedeman gave an account of a very beautiful new species *Hyphessobrycon rubrostigma* [142, Pl. 11], which comes from Colombia and is 9 cm (3½ in) long. The male is distinguished by its high, crescent-shaped dorsal fin. In both sexes there is an ivory-coloured stripe on the anal fin.

Unfortunately aquarists have so far relied almost entirely on imported, wild specimens, since

138

139

breeding presents great difficulties. From the lower waters of the Amazon and the river Tocantin comes the **Flag Tetra**, *Hyphessobrycon hetero-rhabdus* [Pl. 12], which is a popular and commonly kept species. Two rarely kept species – although they are imported from time to time – are *Hyphessobrycon loretoensis* [Pl. 13a], and *Hyphessobrycon peruvianus* [Pl. 13b], which come from the neigh-

142

bourhood of Iquitos on the upper reaches of the Amazon in Peru. These are small — about 4 cm (1½ in) in length — very lively and attractively coloured fishes.

The lower course of the Amazon in the neighbourhood of the Para provides the **Black-line Tetra** or **Scholze's Tetra**, *Hyphessobrycon scholzei* [143].

This species has been kept for several decades although it is no longer popular because of its rather uninteresting colouring.

Hasemania marginata [144], a Characin which lacks the usual adipose fin, inhabits the waters of south-east Brazil. It is about 4 cm (1½ in) long. This active little fish lays sticky, coffee-brown eggs.

9   Serpae Tetra *(Hyphessobrycon callistus serpae)*

10 *Hyphessobrycon 'robertsi'*

147

The **Black Phantom Tetra,** *Megalamphodus megalopterus* [145], is very decorative. It comes from the Matto Grosso. A striking feature of the male is its high dorsal and anal fins. The females have reddish abdominal and dorsal fins, which in the males are grey to black. The **Red Phantom Tetra,** *Megalamphodus sweglesi* [146, Pl. 16], is a close relative. Its principal colouring is light orange and it is extremely difficult to keep. Picture 147 shows a pair of hybrids arising from a cross between a female *Hyphessobrycon rosaceus* and a male *Megalamphodus megalopterus*. In the first generation the hybrids resemble their mother in body shape, but have inherited the male's black spots.

148

In subterranean waters near San Luis Potosi in Mexico lives a blind cave Tetra, the **Blind Cave-fish,** *Anoptichthys jordani* [148], whose evolution can be traced from the genus *Astyanax* which inhabits surface waters of that area and Central and South America. The adult fishes are up to 12 cm (5 in) long. Their lack of eyes gives them an odd appearance. In aquaria they will eat plants quite readily although in the wild they are carnivorous and tend to take the eggs of the other inhabitants of the aquarium. In order to keep them it is necessary to have hard water and the comparatively high temperature of 26–27°C, to which

they are accustomed in their native surroundings. When the fry emerge from the eggs they have quite normally developed eyes with a black pigmentation [149]. However, after eighteen days a deformation of the eye can already be perceived in cross-section [150]: the eye is flattened and the eyeball is covered with an opaque interstitial tissue. The eye does not grow beyond this point and is steadily reduced in size underneath the skin. At fifty-two days [151] the eye is completely covered by skin. Later still the eye, by this time shrunk to a size of only 0.2 cm ($^1/_{12}$ in), acquires a thick covering of fat.

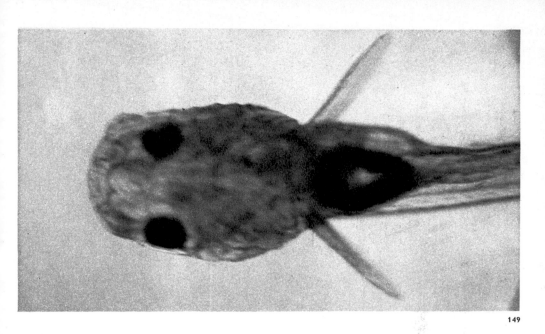

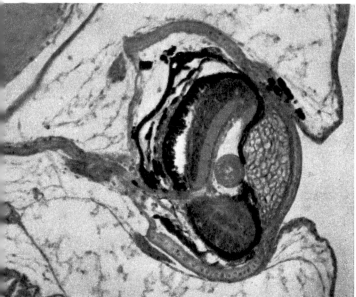

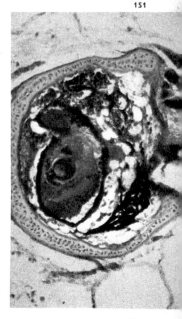

154

The **Silver Tetra**, *Ctenobrycon spilurus* [152], comes from the northern part of South America. This species is easy to keep although it is not particularly popular owing to its comparatively large dimensions – 9 cm (3½ in) – and its uniform silvery colour. A more interesting Characin is the **Swordtail Characin** *(Corynopoma riisei)*, a translucent, light greeny-brown fish with colourless fins [153]. The males have long projections from their gill covers which sometimes extend as far as the root of the dorsal fin. During the dainty courtship display, the male excites the female with the projections on his gill cover. Later he deposits semen in spermatophores around the urogenital opening of the female. Fertilization takes place internally and suffices for the spawning of several batches of fertilized eggs at different intervals.

Ephippicharax orbicularis [154] is a very common species in South America, particularly in Guyana and the Amazon river system. This fish is about 12 cm (5 in) long. Nothing is known about the secondary sexual differences between males and females, and little about the biology of these fishes.

155

Undoubtedly among the most popular aquarium Characins are the species belonging to *Cheirodon* and related genera. The **Neon Tetra,** *Cheirodon (Paracheirodon) innesi* [Pl. 14], was discovered in the upper waters of the Amazon in 1936. Attempts to keep and breed this fish met with many setbacks and difficulties. Not until after the Second World War did breeders meet with any real success. The fish spawn in soft, slightly acid water beside water plants. Picture 155 is of a spawning pair, while picture 156 shows the band at the tail end of the body of both male and female. The small, glass-like eggs attach themselves to water plants [157],

and unless the parents are promptly removed after spawning they eat their offspring with relish. Another beautiful Tetra is the **Cardinal Tetra,** *Cheirodon (Lamprocheirodon) axelrodi* [Pl. 15], which was discovered in 1956 in the upper waters of the Rio Negro and was at first known under the designation *Hyphessobrycon cardinalis.* It has crimson-red colouring, extending from the tail to the gills, with a glittering green band down the back which is broader and more attractive than that of the previous species. The Cardinal Tetra grows to a length of 4 cm (1½ in). It has been kept in captivity with only partial success.

158

All members of the genus *Pyrrhulina* have comparatively long thin bodies. They are natives of the Amazon basin. The **Short Pyrrhulina,** *Pyrrhulina brevis* [158], has a series of red spots, while the dark marking on the dorsal fin of the male has a white border. The species *Pyrrhulina metae* [159] has a characteristic zig-zag stripe along the side of its body. The **Black-banded Pyrrhulina,** *Pyrrhulina nigrofasciata* [160], is somewhat smaller, being about 6 cm (2½ in) long. It was widely kept and reared in captivity although it later became scarce.

It requires a water temperature of about 26°C for spawning. The parents lay the eggs on the upper side of large and carefully cleaned leaves. Far from consuming his offspring the father takes such care of his progeny that after spawning he chases even the mother away. The **Striped Pyrrhulina,** *Pyrrhulina vittata* [161], grows to a length of up to 7 cm (3 in). The upper fork of the tail fin of the male is considerably extended. The Striped Pyrrhulina is kept in much the same way as the preceding species.

159

162

The breeding habits of the **Spraying Characin,** *Copeina arnoldi* [162], are unusual. The fishes leap out of the water and lay their eggs on the underside of broad leaves overhanging the water. In order to prevent them from drying out, the male sprays the eggs with his tail until the fry emerge and fall off the leaf into the water. A native of the lower course of the Amazon is the **Beautiful-scaled Characin,** *Copeina callolepis* [163], on each scale of which is a shining red dot. The **Red-spotted**

Copeina, *Copeina guttata,* is a large Characin from the central Amazon; it grows to a length of some 15 cm (6 in). After a lively courtship near the river bottom, the eggs are laid in sand. The display by which the male attracts the female is shown [164]. During spawning the male presses himself close to the female [165], and during the actual process of laying the male often takes up a protective position. The **Emperor Tetra,** *Nematobrycon palmeri* [Pl. 17b], is remarkable for

164

its emerald green eyes. It comes from Colombia and is about 6 cm (2½ in) long. In the middle of the tail fin of the male there is an extended black ray.

The typical position of this fish is head downwards. The Emperor Tetra is a frustrating fish to keep and breed.

165

The African **Arnold's Red-eyed Characin,** *Arnoldichthys spilopterus* [Pl. 17a], has only recently been successfully reared in captivity. This fish, 7 cm (3 in) long, is a native of tropical West Africa from Lagos to the Niger estuary and has a brilliant, rainbow colouring.

168

The iridescent red film over the eye is a characteristic feature of the **Long-finned Characin,** *Alestes
longipinnis* [168]. The natural habitat of this
species is in tropical West Africa from Sierra Leone
down to the Congo. It is 13 cm (5 in) in length.
Although it is sometimes kept in captivity it has

not yet been successfully bred. The species *Alestes
nurse* [169] is distributed from the Nile to Senegal.
It grows as long as 25 cm (10 in) and only the young
specimens are suitable for keeping in aquaria.
Insects provide their staple diet.
A more popular species is the **Yellow Congo**

169

Characin, *Alestopetersius caudalis* [170], which is a native of the lower Congo basin. It is only 7 cm (3 in) long. This lively but peaceable little fish is easy to keep in company with other species in the tank. By contrast the **Pike Characin,** *Hepsetus odoe* [171], is an uncommonly aggressive and predatory creature of some 35 cm (14 in) in length. Its range lies between Senegal and the Zambezi. If it is to be kept in captivity it requires a large aquarium, a water temperature of 26–28°C, and a plentiful supply of living fishes or even pieces of horsemeat for food.

172

Micralestes acutidens [172] has been introduced to aquaria in one or two instances and has even been successfully bred. Not only is it common in rivers around the Nile, the Niger, and the Zambezi, but it also exists in a number of differently coloured forms. It is approximately 6 cm (2½ in) in length.

The **Congo Tetra**, *Micralestes interruptus* [173], a popular species – although hard to keep – from the Congo basin, grows to somewhat larger dimensions. It is a bronze colour with a greenish sheen. The males have magnificent, wavy, bent dorsal and anal fins.

173

11   *Hyphessobrycon rubrostigma*

12   Flag Tetra *(Hyphessobrycon heterorhabdus)*

174

The family **Anostomidae** comes from Central and South America. Its members are distinguished by an elongated body and their habit of swimming obliquely head downwards. The larger species are often of local economic significance. In western Guyana and in the Amazon above Manaos lives the **Striped Anostomus**, *Anostomus anostomus* [174], which is some 14 cm (5½ in) in length. The basic

175

colouring of its fins is red with a greater or lesser tinge of violet. This hardy and peaceful fish is particularly suitable for home aquaria.

The **Three-spot Anostomus,** *Anostomus trimaculatus* [175], which grows to a length of up to 20 cm (8 in) is from the lower Amazon.

177

An extremely popular species among aquarists is the **Spotted Headstander,** *Chilodus punctatus* [176], which is a native of the waters of the Orinoco, Rio Negro, and the central and upper waters of the Amazon. It is up to 7 cm (3 in) long. The eggs of this fish are rather large and brownish in colour. The young fishes should be fed at first on very fine powdered food consisting chiefly of rotifers and *Cyclops* nauplii. *Leporinus fasciatus* [177] comes from Guyana and the rivers between

178

179

the Orinoco and the Plate. Its body, 30 cm (12 in) long, bears nine dark vertical stripes, the first of which crosses the eye.

Leporinus pellegrini [178] was first recognized by Steindachner; he considered it to be a near relative of *Leporinus fasciatus* on the grounds of the anatomy of the jaws. It is of inconspicuous colouring.

Leporinus striatus [179] comes from the Matto Grosso, the Marañon, and the river Magdalena. It may be 25 cm (10 in) long. The dark brown, lateral stripes grow lighter towards the belly. No secondary sexual differences in colouring are known.

Some years ago the species *Curimatopsis evelynae* [180] of the family **Curimatidae** was imported to Europe. In the wild it lives principally in the upper waters of the river Méta – a tributary of the Orinoco – in company with *Megalamphodus sweglesi*, *Cheirodon axelrodi*, and a whole host of other Characins. This lively little fish, which is only some 4.5 cm (1½ in) long, has not yet been bred successfully in captivity.

181

The family **Hemiodontidae** consists of South American species which are distinguished from other Characins by their toothless lower jaw. *Hemiodus unimaculatus* [181] comes from the Amazon basin and is 16 cm (6 in) long. This long, narrow, elegant fish is only occasionally imported and has not yet been successfully bred. An interesting bottom-living species, *Characidium fasciatum* [182], is found in all the waters from the Orinoco down to the Plate, and is 10 cm (4 in) in length.

182

183

184

These fishes rest on their broad pectoral fins as if leaning on elbows and move in a characteristic jerky fashion. They prefer live food, especially Tubifex worms. Occasionally they have been successfully reared in captivity.

The same family also contains small, brightly coloured fishes, belonging to the genus *Nannostomus*, which are very popular in aquaria. The **Golden Pencilfish,** *Nannostomus beckfordi*, has a special daylight colouring [183]. If a light is shone on this fish at night it can be seen in its 'night clothes' [184]. *Nannostomus beckfordi* is a native of west Guyana, where it grows to a length of 6.5 cm (2½ in). It requires soft water if kept in captivity.

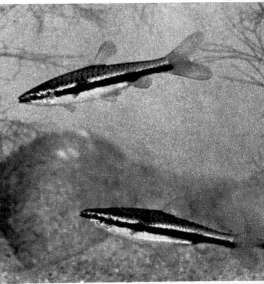

A related species is the **Two-banded Pencilfish,**
Nannostomus bifasciatus [185], from Surinam, which
is 6 cm (2½ in) long. The central waters of the
Amazon and the Rio Negro are the home of the
Three-banded Pencilfish, *Nannostomus trifascia-*
tus [186], which grows to the same length as the

186

13a *Hyphessobrycon loretoensis*
13b *Hyphessobrycon peruvianus*

15 Cardinal Tetra *(Cheirodon axelrodi)*

14 Neon Tetra *(Cheirodon innesi)*

16 Red Phantom Tetra *(Megalamphodus sweglesi)*

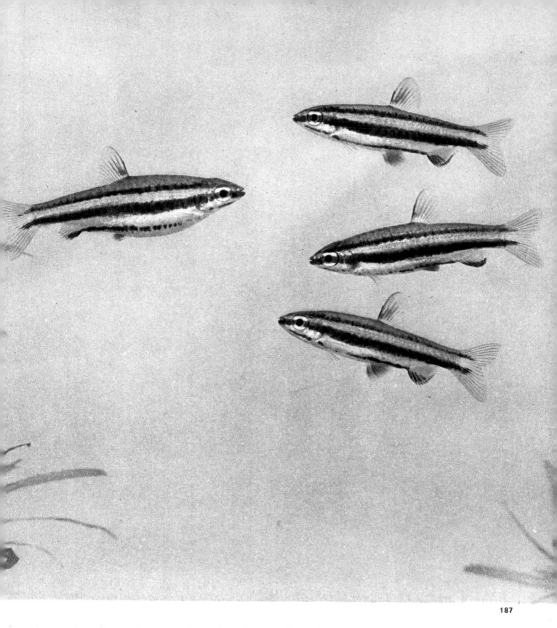

187

previous species. The smallest – maximum length 4 cm (1½ in) – and most popular species is the **Dwarf Pencilfish,** *Nannostomus marginatus*, from Surinam and Guyana. Picture 187 shows three males and one female. The males are characterized by rounded anal fins with a black border. The anal fin of the female, on the other hand, is triangular and has a transparent border.

188

189

The act of spawning is very similar in all species of Pencilfishes. A male is seen here [188] following a female who is looking for a suitable place to lay her eggs. In every act of spawning only one or two eggs are ejected; their total number rarely exceeds 100. In the actual act of spawning [189] the male presses the lower part of his body against the flank of the female. The fry, up to the age of two to three weeks, have a somewhat ragged appearance [190] with their brown flecked bodies and fins. At the age of about twenty-five days [191] they begin to take on the colouring of the adult fish. After a further five to six weeks the colouring becomes lighter and the lateral stripe more regular [192].

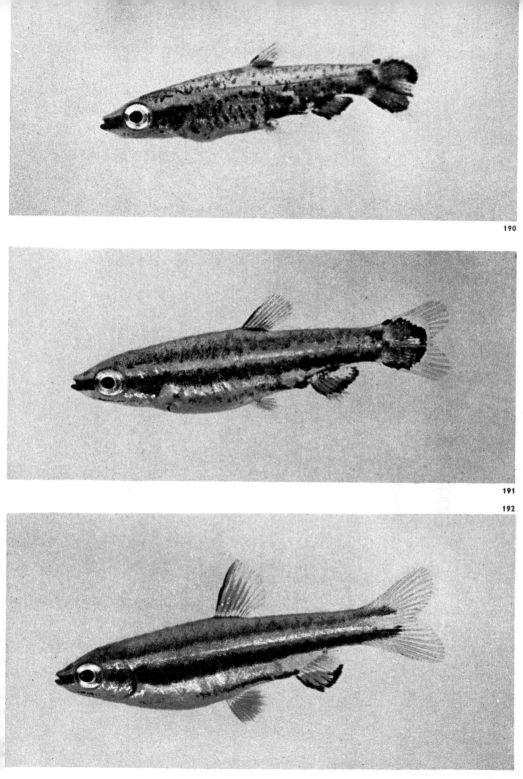

190

191

192

193

Poecilobrycon harrisoni [193] comes from Guyana, particularly from the neighbourhood of Christianburg. It is 6 cm (2½ in) long. The **Tube-mouthed Pencilfish,** *Nannobrycon eques,* swims in a slanted position with its head upwards. It is present in large numbers in the waters of the Amazon and achieves a length of 5 cm (2 in). It readily reproduces in captivity. It is at its best in a tank which contains only a few fishes of the same species. Picture 194 shows the typical position of the male above the female before the beginning of spawning. The eggs are usually attached to the underside of the leaves of a water plant. Spawning is not always successful. In picture 195 the female lies along the central rib of the leaf to spawn, while two males remain on one side looking on. Some authors place both *Poecilobrycon harrisoni* and *Nannobrycon eques* in the genus *Nannostomus.*

The family **Citharinidae** comes from central Africa. Larger species are found in zoo aquaria; only the smaller species are kept in private aquaria. *Distichodus antonii* [196], which is up to 55 cm (22 in) long, is a native of the Congo river system. It is an inconspicuous grey-green in colour with a few faint, diagonal stripes. *Distichodus rostratus* [197] comes from the rivers of the Nile, Senegal, and Niger systems. Its body is long – 60 cm (24 in) – and has a silvery sheen, sometimes with a dark brown film covering it. Young specimens are covered in a large number of diagonal stripes. The extended, forward-tilted mouth is characteristic.

The **One-striped African Characin**, *Nannaethiops unitaeniatus* [198], lives in a great many waters in equatorial Africa, from the White Nile to the west coast. Its length is 6.5 cm (2½ in). Its monotonous, grey-green colouring makes it a comparatively unpopular aquarium fish. However, it has been successfully bred; the placid females are very fertile.

199

A more popular, but less prolific, species is **Ansorge's Characin,** *Neolebias ansorgei* [199], which is a native of the waters of central Africa and is only 3.5 cm (1½ in) long. The green, opalescent body is splendidly contrasted by the red fins. This fish is resistant to changes in the composition of the water, but in hard water it is pale and rarely shows the true beauty of its colouring.

200

The genus *Nannocharax* is spread throughout west Africa: its distribution extends from Senegal and Gambia along the upper Niger, down through equatorial Africa, to the Ogowe and the Congo. Most species prefer sandbanks and crystal-clear streams and rivers. Of the whole genus only the species *Nannocharax ansorgei* [200] is found in sluggish or standing water. This fish grows to a length of some 5 cm (2 in). In captivity it is best suited by dimly lit tanks. Its principal diet consists of tubifex worms and on occasion the larvae of mosquitos and midges.

Members of the family **Gasteropelecidae** (Hatchet-fishes) are found from Panama to the river Plate. The back is almost straight, but the belly is distended in an arch by the enormous development of the pectoral girdle and muscles. By rapid beating of their pectoral fins they are able to leave the water and glide above the surface for a distance of 3–5 cm (1½–2 in). The **Common Hatchetfish**, *Gasteropelecus sternicla* [201], lives in the Amazon and is 6.5 cm (2½ in) long. The fish is yellowish in colouring, although in bright light it seems to be a light silver-grey.

202

203

The **Marbled Hatchetfish**, *Carnegiella strigata* [202], which likewise comes from the Amazon and Guyana, lives in small jungle streams and pools. As in other members of this genus the adipose fin is absent. The Marbled Hatchetfish has a narrow, dark band with a silver margin along the length of its body. The smallest species is the **Black-winged Hatchetfish**, *Carnegiella marthae* [203], from the waters of Venezuela and Peru, the Brazilian part of the Amazon, the Rio Negro, and the Orinoco. It is only 3.5 cm (1½ in) long and, as far as colouring is concerned, is the most attractive of the three species. Hatchetfishes feed on insects — mostly fruit flies, small beetles and mosquito larvae which they pick from the surface of the water. Some species have already been bred in captivity.

The suborder **Gymnotoidei** (Knife-fishes) is different from other members of the Cypriniformes in that the anal opening is in the region of the throat or in the middle of the lower jaw. The tail fin and the pelvic fins are absent or atrophied. On the other hand the anal fin, which is the chief organ of locomotion, is strongly developed. The **Green Knife-fish**, *Eigenmannia virescens* [204], from the family **Rhamphichthyidae**, is an inhabitant of the waters of South America, from the north down to the river Plate and westwards to the Magdalena. It grows to a length of 45 cm (18 in). The body has an iridescent blue sheen over

a pale flesh colour. In its natural environment it prefers slow-flowing rivers, lagoons, and shallow lakes with plentiful plant growth. The anal fin of the adult fish has a black edge.

The **Electric Eel**, *Electrophorus electricus* [205], from the family **Electrophoridae**, is found in pools and the deeper parts of small rivers and streams of the Orinoco basin, Guyana, and the lower and central Amazon. It is 2.5 m (8 ft) long. It breathes not only with its gills but also through the mucous membrane of the palate, which is

206

abundantly supplied with blood vessels: the fish takes in air with its mouth. The electric organs are modified muscle fibres; they can produce shocks of up to 800 volts. Electric Eels can be dangerous even to large swimming animals the size of a horse. They normally use their electric organs to stun fishes which are then eaten.

The suborder **Cyprinoidei,** containing the Carp group, is characterized by an absence of teeth in the jaws. Instead the fishes have one, two or three rows of heavy teeth on a pair of bones in the pharynx (the pharyngeal teeth). Fishes of this suborder are present in Europe, Asia, North America, and Africa. The suborder is not repre-

sented in South America, Madagascar, or Australia. The largest number of species belong to the Carp family, **Cyprinidae,** which is most strongly represented in southern Asia and tropical Africa and to which many familiar North American and European fishes belong. The genus *Rutilus* which belongs to this family is characterized by a single row of pharyngeal teeth. The **Roach,** *Rutilus rutilus* [206, 208], lives in relatively slow flowing rivers and lakes and generally feeds on insect larvae and invertebrates. It grows to a maximum length of 40 cm (16 in) and weighs up to 1.5 kg (3¼ lb). There is a large number of subspecies distributed throughout Europe — with the exception of the Pyrenees and the Balkan Peninsula — and Siberia. On the

208

Baltic coast it sometimes swims down river into brackish estuaries. It can be crossed with the Rudd, Bream, and Tench, and is usually fished for in the pools and lower courses of rivers [207]. Roach spawn in spring on flooded meadows when the water temperature reaches 14–16°C, or on the submerged vegetation along the banks. A female contains up to 100,000 eggs. Related fishes are found in the rivers flowing into the Caspian and Black Seas. The most familiar of these is *Rutilus frisii*. An isolated form from the lakes of Bavaria is the 'Frauenfisch', *Rutilus frisii meidingeri* [209]. The picture shows quite clearly the so-called spawning rash which consists of white horny blisters along the head and sides of the fishes in the spawning season. These are most pronounced in the males and, although sometimes not so prominent, are found in most cyprinid fishes. *Rutilus frisii* is up to 1 m (3 ft) long and 7 kg (15 lb) in weight. The **Moderlieschen**, *Leucaspius delineatus*

209

[210], has a brilliant, silvery-blue band running along the length of the body. It grows to a length of about 9 cm ($3\frac{1}{2}$ in) and spawns in summer. The eggs are attached in loops and spirals around the leaves and stems of water plants. Until they hatch they are watched over by the male. The Moderlieschen is found in still and slow-moving waters from the Rhine to the Volga, and the Danube to the Don.

The genus *Leuciscus* consists of many species which have a long body covered in comparatively large scales, a short anal fin, and pharyngeal teeth in two rows. The **Dace**, *Leuciscus leuciscus* [211], lives chiefly in clean, running water. Its habitat in Europe stretches from the Pyrenees and the Alps to the northern part of the Urals. It occurs throughout England. It is 30 cm (12 in) long, and 0.5 kg (1 lb) in weight. The free edge of the anal fin is indented. By contrast the **Chub**, *Leuciscus cephalus*, is characterized by a convex anal fin.

212

213

214

Picture 212 shows a yearling. All its fins are red or at least tinged with red and it is found throughout northern Europe, in Asia to south of the Euphrates, and in the east as far as the Dvina, and the rivers flowing into the Caspian Sea. Its length is 80 cm (32 in), its weight 5 kg (11 lb), and it is omnivorous. The young fishes live in shoals, but in later life they become solitary and can be found in many different kinds of water.

The **Orfe** or **Ide,** *Leuciscus Idus* [213, Pl.18a], is differentiated from the related Chub by having smaller scales and a higher back. Its distribution stretches from the Rhine to the Lena, and from the Danube to the Ural. It measures 60 cm (24 in) and weighs

4 kg (9 lb). A red form, the **Golden Orfe,** *Leuciscus idus* var. *orfus* [213, 214], is bred in fish ponds, but is not found in the wild. In spite of the wide geographical distribution of the Orfe it shows little variation.

Leuciscus souffia agassizi [215], an inhabitant of the upper Rhine and of the Danube in north-west Rumania, has a very slender body. During the spawning season it is one of the most attractively coloured members of the Carp group. The males have a longitudinal, black band with a violet iridescence on the upper part of the body. It is some 20 cm (8 in) long. Similar forms are found in southern France and northern Italy.

215

The natural habitat of the **Minnow**, *Phoxinus phoxinus* [216], is in sandy or stony bottomed streams and upper reaches of rivers. It occurs throughout Europe north of the Pyrenees and in most of the British Isles. The Minnow is a small fish – only 12 cm (4½ in) long – and plays an important part in the diet of Trout. The lateral line is not continuous. Except in the spawning season sexual dimorphism is only apparent in the shape and size of the pectoral fins. During spawning, however, the male acquires striking colouring and develops a rash of spawning tubercules, especially on his head. A related form is found in stagnant waters, especially muddy areas overgrown with waterplants, and rivers flowing into the Arctic Ocean and the Baltic Sea. This is the drab-

coloured *Phoxinus percnurus* [217], which is particularly common in the neighbourhood of Crakow, Poznan, and Danzig.

The **Rudd**, *Scardinius erythrophthalmus* [218], lives in slow-moving rivers and lakes of central and western Europe and is widespread in Britain. It is 35 cm (14 in) long and 1 kg (2 lb) in weight, and resembles the Roach, from which it may be distinguished by a higher back and a narrow, oblique mouth. It feeds partly on water plants but especially on surface-living insects and invertebrates. Hybrids with Bream and Roach are known.

The **Asp**, *Aspius aspius* [219], is present in central Europe and southern Sweden eastwards to the

220

USSR. It is also found in waters flowing into the Arctic Ocean. It is sometimes more than 80 cm (32 in) long and 12–14 kg (26–30 lb) in weight. Young fishes feed on plankton, but adult specimens eat small fishes. The Asp lives in shoals close to the surface in the larger rivers of Europe. When attacking its prey it often leaps clear of the water. It has considerable economic value in the USSR and makes a good sporting fish.

The **Tench**, *Tinca tinca* [220], is found in Europe, in Siberia, and in the Caucasus. Fully grown, it is 64 cm (25 in) long and weighs some 7.5 kg (16 lb). The Tench is a peaceable fish, typically living close to the bottom, where it feeds on small animals and plants. It displays striking sexual dimorphism. In the male the first two rays of the pelvic fins are very thick and this fin is long enough to completely cover the anal opening. It is a popular fish with anglers, who catch it in still pools and river reaches [221]. Where it is permitted, a form of drop net is often used to catch Tench [222]. Tench are often raised in fishponds along with Carp. They grow slowly but can withstand low oxygen levels.

222

The genus *Chondrostoma* contains some eighteen species which are found throughout Europe (with the exceptions of the British Isles, northern Germany and Scandinavia) and in the waters flowing into the Baltic, the Caspian, and the Black Seas. It is not found on the Elbe although it is present in the Rhine to the west and in the Oder and the Vistula to the east.

The **Nase,** *Chondrostoma nasus,* is a migratory fish living principally in central Europe in higher reaches of rivers. It lives near the bottom where it feeds not only on the plant growth there, but apparently also on small creatures living on the plants. It is 40 cm (16 in) long and 1 kg (2 lb) in weight. Nase are often found in shoals. It is seldom fished for by anglers.

The **Gudgeon,** *Gobio gobio* [223, 224], is familiar in England and is encountered in Europe and northern Asia. It is generally found in shoals near the bottom, among rocks, plant roots, and other irregularities of the river bed. The Gudgeon has an average length of 20 cm (8 in). It is greenish-brown on the back with small, dark spots, shading into greenish-yellow sides and a silvery-yellow belly.

The **Barbel,** *Barbus barbus,* lives in Europe, with the exception of Scandinavia and the southernmost parts of the continent. The central reaches of fast-flowing rivers with stony bottoms are typical Barbel waters. It feeds principally on fauna of the river bed and also on small fishes and fish eggs. Spawning takes place in spring (April–May) on gravel bottoms. The Barbel is a lively and powerful

224

225

17a Arnold's Red-eyed Characin *(Arnoldichthys spilopterus)*
17b Emperor Tetra *(Nematobrycon palmeri)*

18a Orfe (*Leuciscus idus*)
18b Tiger Barb (*Puntius/Barbus tetrazona*)

226

fish — it is 1 m (3 ft) long and weighs 16 kg (35 lb) — highly valued as sport by anglers [225]. In hunting for its prey the Barbel uses the two pairs of barbels on the upper lip [227]. This means that it will feed and take a bait even when the river is in spate.

The **Silver Bream**, *Blicca bjoerkna* [226], lives in slow-flowing waters. The paired fins and the anal fin are tinged with red at the roots. It may grow to a length of 35 cm (14 in) and weigh 400 gm (1 lb). It is widely distributed across northern Europe, southern Sweden and the rivers of the Baltic, the Caspian, and the Black Seas, but it is found only in eastern England. Anglers find it less shy than the **Common** or **Bronze Bream**,

227

228

Abramis brama [228], which generally lives in the same area. This is a high-backed fish, present throughout Europe except in the Pyrenees, and in the Appennine and Balkan peninsulas. In eastern Europe large specimens weighing about 4–5 kg (9–11 lb) are caught at night in reservoirs with special seine nets [229], usually together with Roach, Carp, and other cyprinid fishes. A single

catch ending at dawn [230] yields anything up to a ton. In view of the economic importance of the Bream, fishermen have become interested in breeding it artificially. Artificial spawning beds [231] are constructed of pine twigs and moss, which are then laid and secured on the bottom of controlled rivers, where the fish use them to lay their eggs. An egg laden bed is shown in picture 232.

233

The **Zope**, *Abramis ballerus* [233], occurs in the
Danube basin and the continental rivers of the
North Sea and the Baltic from the Rhine to the
Neva. It has a projecting mouth and achieves
a length of some 35 cm (14 in).

The **Bitterling**, *Rhodeus sericeus amarus* [234],
which is about 8 cm (3 in) long, is widespread in
northern Europe, along the eastern Baltic and the
catchment areas of the Black Sea and the Caspian.
It prefers still waters in the lower reaches of
rivers, backwaters with a soft mud bottom, and
also stagnant creeks and ponds in places where
there are no predatory fish. During the breeding
season, the female develops a 5–6 cm (2 in) long
ovipositor which she inserts between the valves
of Swan Mussels (*Anodonta* and *Unio*) in order to
lay her eggs where they are protected. The colouring of the males is strikingly beautiful. The Bitterling show their appreciation of the mussels'
hospitality by acting as host in turn to their parasitic larvae (glochidia).

235

236

237

The **Crucian Carp,** *Carassius carassius*, grows to
a length of 45 cm (18 in). Its mouth has no barbels.
It is an inhabitant of western Europe and Russia
as far east as the Lena, but is not found in the Aral
Sea basin, nor further east. The Crucian Carp
dwells in quiet backwaters of the lower reaches
of rivers and is resistant to low levels of oxygen.
In unfavourable conditions the Crucian Carp is
long bodied and thin [235]. This grows slowly and

achieves a length of only 10–15 cm (4–6 in). However, in the favourable conditions of fish ponds it
grows into a highbacked form [236] which is
regarded as typical.

The **Goldfish,** *Carassius auratus*, is found in China,
Manchuria and Japan. In China it is kept along with
Carp in ornamental ponds, for example the Lu-cha
Garden [237]. There is a centuries-old tradition

of artificial culture of these fishes, and numerous races have been developed. Picture 238 shows the gate of the Pei-Hai Kung-Yüan garden in Peking where the goldfish-breeding centre is situated. The **Veil-tail,** into the breeding of which a great deal of effort and money is invested, is found in a wide variety of colours — grey [239], white [240], black, red, and other bright colours — and likewise in a wide variety of forms — the

Egg-fish, which has no dorsal fins, the **Telescope Veil-tail,** the **Celestial,** the **Comet,** and the **Lionhead.** In the Far East, Europe and America much care is taken in breeding these varieties. In pictures 241 and 242 white Veil-tails are seen spawning. Unfortunately, even with the most careful breeding, a large percentage of the offspring revert to the original form, or do not have all parts of their bodies fully developed according to

241

242

243

international standards. For this reason the breeding of Veil-tails is always a great test of patience.

The original distribution of the **Carp**, *Cyprinus carpio carpio* [243], lies in tributaries of the Danube and the rivers of the Black Sea but because of its hardiness it has been spread the world over by man. The Carp's long body is covered in large scales; the mouth has three rows of pharyngeal teeth and two pairs of barbels.

244

245

246

In the course of several centuries a large number of races of Carp has arisen, chiefly through the agency of fish breeders, for example the **Scaly** Carp [244], a high-backed form [245], the **Leather Carp** (a scaleless variety), the **Mirror Carp** [248], which has a few scales in the middle of its body,

and the **Golden Carp** [249]. The breeding of Carp in fishponds is undertaken mainly in the land-locked eastern countries of Europe. After the water level has been lowered to a certain minimum depth they are caught in nets which are dragged out with ropes [246]. The netted Carp [247] are weighed

248

out on the bank immediately. After the autumn
fishing the major part of the catch does not go
straight to the market, but is sent on to fish
tanks or put out in smaller ponds which are kept
supplied with pure, well-oxygenated water. There
they remain until the Christmas market.

19   Five-banded Barb *(Puntius/Barbus pentazona)*

20   Harlequin Fish (*Rasbora heteromorpha*)

250

Ctenopharyngodon idella [250] is a member of the Carp family of considerable economic importance in China and Japan. Its weight is up to 32 kg (70 lb) and its length over 1 m (3 ft). Its eggs are pelagic. It feeds on the higher water plants and grows very quickly. For this reason it is considered to be of service in the battle against the choking and filling in of small ponds by vegetation.

The **White-cloud Mountain Minnow**, *Tanichthys albonubes* [251], lives in the Canton province of China. This 4 cm (1½ in) long fish is prized by experienced aquarists. It is a sturdy little fish and will survive winter temperatures as low as 5°C. For spawning, however, it requires warmer waters, in the order of 20–22°C. Its fry are very small, although they feed not only on the smallest live animals, especially rotifers, but also on a variety of ground artificial foods, or the yolk of hardboiled egg. Picture 252 shows the act of spawning in progress in a tangle of water plants. The male embraces the female's dorsal fin.

253

254

Balantiocheilus melanopterus [253] comes from the waters of Thailand, Borneo, and Sumatra. It is present both in flowing water and in a variety of pond waters. Water temperatures of 23–25°C are recommended if this fish is to be bred. Adult specimens are only suitable for large public aquaria, being about 35 cm (14 in) long. The **Indian Glass Barb,** *Laubuca dadiburjori* [254], lives in waters in the neighbourhood of Bombay in India, and is a lively fish growing to a length of 4–5 cm (1½–2 in).

Its bright colouring only achieves its full brilliance when the fish is kept with others of its kind.

The **Glass Barb,** *Oxygaster oxygastroides* [255] comes from Thailand and the Greater Sunda Islands, where it lives in still waters. It is abundant in its natural habitat, where it achieves a length of 20 cm (8 in). In captivity it is significantly smaller. Sexually mature fishes have an extended anal fin, and the young are transparent.

255

Among the Indian and oriental cyprinid fishes the lively, brightly coloured, and resilient little fishes of the genus *Brachydanio*, enjoy great popularity among aquarists. Some ichthyologists regard this genus as being no more than a subgenus of *Danio*: they are clearly closely related. Among their number is the rainbow-coloured **Pearl Danio**, *Brachydanio albolineatus*. It comes from western

India and Sumatra and grows to a length of 5.5 cm (2 in). Even in stagnant tap water its care presents few difficulties provided that it is kept at a temperature of 23–26°C.

From the islands Koh Yao Yai and Koh Yao Noi in Thailand comes *Brachydanio kerri* [256], which is about 4 cm (1½ in) long. Its fins are yellowish and both pairs of barbels are comparatively short.

260

261

The **Spotted Danio,** Brachydanio nigrofasciatus [257], is a very popular species which comes from upper Burma, where it lives in small rivers and lakes. It is 4 cm (1½ in) long and has one pair of barbels. Its belly is orange to yellowish-white, and underneath the lowest longitudinal band there is a row of dark spots. This fish is not very fertile, and one spawning yields at most seventy offspring.

By contrast the **Leopard Danio,** Brachydanio frankei [258], is very widely distributed. It is about 5.5 cm (2 in) long, and its actual place of origin is unknown. The fish is often encountered as a mutation or a cross arising from the Zebra Danio. The **Zebra Danio,** Brachydanio rerio [259], comes from the waters of eastern India. It was first imported to Europe as early as 1905 and since then has enjoyed unflagging popularity. Its length is 4.5 cm (2 in). This unassuming little fish needs a water temperature of 22–24°C for spawning. Picture 260 shows a pair shortly before the act of spawning. In the following picture [261], a pair is captured in the characteristic preparatory position over a tangle of water plants. Brachydanio rerio and Brachydanio frankei can be easily crossed and their offspring are fertile. Picture 262 shows first generation crosses. Picture 263 shows a hybrid of a female Brachydanio rerio and a male Brachydanio nigrofasciatus. This specimen, which is also of the first generation, shows a remarkable blending of the features of the two parents.

The genus Danio contains as the first example Danio regina [264], from southern Thailand. This fish is up to 12 cm (4½ in) long, and is seldom kept. Danio devario [265] comes from a comparatively wide area of India. Its 10 cm (4 in) long body is laterally compressed and has a fairly high back. These fishes are not nearly as popular as their smaller relatives of the genus Brachydanio,

262
263

181

264

The **Giant Danio**, *Danio malabaricus* [267], comes from the west coast of India and from Ceylon. It is an inhabitant of clean, swift-flowing waters, and is 12 cm (4½ in) long. It is sexually mature once it has grown to a length of 6–7 cm (2½ in). The male is narrower and has duller colouring.

The genus *Epalzeorhynchus* is chiefly met with in Sumatra and Borneo; it includes *Epalzeorhynchus*

265

266

kallopterus [266], which is some 14 cm (5½ in) long. The mouth of this narrow fish is set comparatively far back. It takes live food of all kinds and prefers to live near the river bed or close to broad leaves of water plants, supporting itself on its pectoral fins. A related species, *Epalzeorhynchus siamensis* [268], is a native of Thailand and it is differentiated from the preceding species chiefly by its transparent,

267

colourless fins. This fish is only rarely imported and kept in aquaria. In Thailand it is a source of food and widely fished for.

Garra taeniata [269] is completely harmless to other fishes although it is 15 cm (6 in) long. It lives in the waters of Thailand. Its background colouring is a shade of rust brown; the belly is white and the fins are reddish. Algae growing on stones serve as its principal foodstuff. Since it is an inhabitant of torrents and rapids, it uses the sucking disc of its mouth not only to gather algae, but also to keep its position in fast-moving waters.

The **Malayan Flying Barb**, *Esomus malayensis* [270], comes from the Malayan Peninsula and South Vietnam. It is 8 cm (3 in) long. It can be kept with comparative success in captivity but only in large tanks. A single spawning will, as a rule, produce 700 offspring. The fry feed as soon as they are hatched particularly on free-swimming plankton. In Africa and in South and South-East Asia, including the offshore islands, live species of the genus *Labeo*. The **Red-tailed Black 'Shark'**, *Labeo bicolor* [271], comes from mountain streams in Thailand. It is 12 cm (4½ in) long. The mouth is set back and has

272

strongly developed lips forming a sucking disc; the inner part of the disc is equipped with horny ridges and tubercles with which the fish rubs the algae off the river bed. The Red-tailed Black 'Shark' prefers a dimly lit aquarium with dark recesses. There is a wonderful contrast in colouring between the velvet black body and the blood-red tail fin. The **Green Fringed-lip Labeo,** *Labeo frenatus* [272], which is up to 8 cm (3 in) in length, is an inhabitant of northern Thailand. The sides of its body are olive-grey, while the belly is bronze to white. At the root of the tail there is a dark blotch,

273

and in the male the tail fin has a black border. *Labeo erythrurus* is another species from Thailand. It is the same length as, but somewhat narrower, than, *Labeo bicolor*. Its body colouring is light to dark brown, and occasionally blue to black. The belly is lighter and sometimes spotted. The tail

fin is orange to red. In picture 273 a not quite fully grown specimen is shown.

The genus *Puntius* or *Barbus* is confined to the Old World, but its members are to be found in India, Ceylon, South-East Asia, China, and Africa in the most widely different kinds of water. There is

a great deal of confusion about the limits of the genera *Puntius* and *Barbus*, some authors placing all the tropical Barbs in one or other genus. The use here of *Puntius/Barbus* is an attempt to signify alternatives, not recognition of a subgenus. From the south-eastern part of India comes *Puntius/Barbus arulius* [274] with a length of 12 cm (4½ in). A large number of local races are known, distinguishable in form and colouring. In particular, the extended rays of the dorsal fin in the male show striking differences in respect of length and number. This species is rarely found in aquaria and the number of fry originating from a single spawning is also comparatively small. In picture 275 a male is seen taking up his position above the female. In picture 276 the act of spawning is taking place over bare stones. This species is not fussy about the surface over which it spawns: in picture 277, a pair is spawning over some water plants.

Puntius/Barbus barilioides [278] has a narrow body, 8 cm (3 in) long, and comes from Africa. Its colouring is brick-red with several black cross-stripes varying greatly in number. The fish is quite common in aquaria and can be successfully bred. The **Rosy**

276

277

21   Clown Loach (*Botia macracantha*)

22a   Cape Lopez Lyretail *(Aphyosemion australe)*
22b   Calabar Lyretail *(Roloffia liberiense)*

Barb or **Red Barb,** *Puntius/Barbus conchonius* [279], comes from the northern part of the Indian sub-continent, especially Bengal and Assam. In nature it grows to a length of 14 cm (5½ in), but in captivity only reaches 6 cm (2½ in). It is a popular aquarium fish and was introduced to Europe as early as 1903. One advantage in keeping it is that it survives winters in water temperatures as low as 15–16°C unharmed. During the spawning season the male acquires a purple colouring; his dorsal, anal, and pelvic fins are black. An adult female lays several hundreds of glassy eggs.

279

280

281

282

In fresh waters around Singapore and in Borneo lives the **Everett's Barb** or **Clown Barb,** *Puntius/Barbus everetti* [280], which is 13 cm (5 in) long. The care of this attractive, red-coloured fish is not devoid of difficulty. The female should be separated from the male before spawning and fed plentifully on worms and insect larvae with a rich variety of plant food. Spawning can only be achieved in large aquaria with a rich growth of milfoil *(Myriophyllum)*. The tank should be so placed that the morning sun shines into it. Optimum water temperature is 25–27°C. The **Striped Barb** or **Zebra Barb,** *Puntius/Barbus fasciatus,* inhabits the waters of Sumatra, Borneo, and the Malayan Peninsula. Besides this species a further form, known to aquarists as *Puntius/Barbus lineatus* [281], has been introduced from the state of Johore in Malaya. It reproduces prolifically and can be bred easily in captivity.

The **Black-spot Barb,** *Puntius/Barbus filamentosus* [282], comes from south-west India. It is 15 cm (6 in) long. In strong light this barb displays all the colours of the rainbow. Immature specimens are often confused with the species *Puntius/Barbus mahecola,* from which, however, they are distinguishable by the absence of barbels. This latter species possesses a pair of barbels on the upper jaw at the corners of the mouth. Another species from the Malayan Peninsula, also found on the Greater and Lesser Sunda Islands, is the **Spanner Barb,** *Puntius/Barbus lateristriga* [283]. In nature it achieves a length of 18 cm (7 in), but in captivity it is appreciably smaller. Ahl has described a similar barb under the name *Barbus zeleri,* which according to Klausewitz is identical with young specimens

283

284

285

of *Puntius/Barbus lateristriga*. This species has four pairs of barbels and is subject to considerable variations in form and colouring across its wide area of distribution.

The **Black Ruby, Nigger Barb** or **Purple-headed Barb,** *Puntius/Barbus nigrofasciatus* [285] is an unassuming and resilient little fish of only 5 cm (2 in) length. It comes from slow-moving waters of Ceylon. The front half of the male's body is purple during the spawning season and the rear end is velvet black. A water temperature of 15–16°C is sufficient in winter, but for spawning a temperature of about 25°C is necessary. It is particularly suitable for keeping with other species in aquaria. Younger specimens are silvery-grey with dark cross stripes [284].

The **Five-banded Barb,** *Puntius/Barbus pentazona* [286, Pl. 19], lives in fresh waters in Borneo, Sumatra, and the Malayan Peninsula. It, too, is some 5 cm (2 in) long, although the female is noticeably larger than the male. In an environment in which the fish feels at home, this is one of the most gaily coloured of barbs. However, they are shy creatures and therefore difficult to keep, especially when older specimens are put together for pairing. Nevertheless, this barb generally reproduces well, since one spawning sometimes yields 300 to 400 large eggs. The fry are big and can be easily reared to maturity on a powdered protein diet. Picture 287 shows the characteristic manner in which the male embraces the female's dorsal fin during spawning. Barbs like to spawn over a substratum of milfoil [288].

289

The home of the **Sumatra** or **Tiger Barb,** *Puntius/Barbus tetrazona* [289], lies in the waters of Sumatra and Borneo. The male is some 7 cm (3 in) long. Because of its bright colouring this energetic fish is very popular in aquaria. However, it requires the relatively high temperature of about 26–27°C if its colouring is to be displayed to the best advantage [Pl. 18b]. The upper jaw of the male, and often much of the head up to the eyes, is an intense red colour. In contrast to other members of the aquarium community, the Tiger Barb is often aggressive and will bite off the fins of other fishes. It is unfortunately vulnerable to a number of diseases so that very few live to any great age. This factor is offset, however, by the comparative ease of obtaining and rearing the fry. Spawning takes place at a temperature of 24–27°C and is very violent. The fishes seek out particular places to lay their eggs [290], although they frequently move on during the course of spawning. Sometimes they pair close to the surface [291], but will then move on swiftly to settle directly above some aquatic moss (*Fontinalis*) at the bottom of the tank [292]. In recent years an albino form with red eyes [293] has been bred, which flourishes particularly well in a thickly planted tank.

290

291

292

197

293

294

From south-east China comes the **Chinese Half-striped** or **Green Barb,** *Puntius/Barbus semifasciolatus* [294]. Its length is in the order of 7 cm (3 in). In captivity it likes large sunny tanks with a rich plant growth. It is not particularly fussy about the quantity of oxygen, and will survive a winter without harm in spite of significant changes of temperature. It breeds at a temperature of 22–24°C. The male 'stands' or 'dances' in front of the female with his head bent downwards and sideways. Then he darts as quick as an arrow to the side of the female and nudges her with his head

or by blows of his tail fin into the plants. A violent spawning follows.

The **Golden Barb** or **Schubert's Barb,** *Puntius/ Barbus 'schuberti'* [295], is not a wild species. It is believed to have been developed as a hybrid or xanthic form of *Puntius/Barbus semifasciolatus*, or of the **Gold-finned Barb** or **Sachs' Barb,** *Puntius/ Barbus sachsi*. Its golden-yellow colouring is impressive, and for this reason, as well as because of its splendid appearance and the fact that it is easy to keep, it is a very popular fish,

296

Schwanenfeld's Barb, *Puntius/Barbus schwanenfeldi* [296], is considerably larger — 35 cm (14 in) long — than the other barbs. Its fins are brightly coloured in orange, yellow, black and green, which makes it a splendid showpiece for larger aquaria and zoos. Sexual dimorphism has not yet been described. It prefers soft-bottomed aquaria. It is not fussy about its choice of food and grows quickly on a plentiful diet: breeders have little difficulty with it

An attractive and popular Barb is **Stoliczka's Barb**, *Puntius/Barbus stoliczkanus* [298], which is 6 cm (2½ in) long and lives in the waters of Burma. It was first brought to Europe in 1925 and since then has been kept widely in aquaria. A temperature of 24–26°C is necessary for spawning. Young fishes are hatched after twenty-four to thirty hours.

The **Two-Spot** or **Tic–tac-toe Barb**, *Puntius/Barbus ticto* [297], is widely distributed throughout India and Ceylon. This specimen reaches a length of 10 cm (4 in), and has an incomplete lateral line with pores present on only six to eight scales – its particular characteristic feature. It was brought to Europe in 1903. It is simple to keep and during winter a temperature of 14–16°C is sufficient.

299

300

The **Cherry Barb,** *Puntius/Barbus titteya* [229],
lives in shady streams in Ceylon and is 5 cm (2 in)
long. In aquaria it is extremely shy and retiring
and always seeks out dark hiding places. A number
of forms occur in nature, of which some are distinguished by the bright red colouring of the male.
Up to 250 offspring are produced by a single
spawning, and at a temperature of 25–26°C they
hatch about twenty-four hours after successful
fertilization of the eggs. During the spawning
season it is recommended that the young fish
should be fed with white worms (enchytraeids)
to prevent them from eating their own eggs. The
head-downwards position of the spawning pair
[300] is somewhat unusual.

The elegant, delicate, little fishes of the genus
Rasbora have their distribution in East Africa,
southern and east Asia, Indonesia, and the Philippines. The majority of species live in shoals which
swim close to the water's surface. *Rasbora bora-
petensis* [301] is an inhabitant of Thailand and is
about 5 cm (2 in) long. This fish has occasionally
been imported. So far nothing is known of its
sexual dimorphism or of its reproductive biology.
Adult specimens can be kept without trouble for
many years in captivity.

The **Harlequin Fish** or **Red Rasbora,** *Rasbora
heteromorpha* [302, Pl 30], is very popular. It
comes from the Malayan Peninsula, Thailand, and

301

eastern Sumatra. It was imported to Europe in 1906. For a long time it presented great difficulties in care and breeding for the eggs and fry require soft, slightly acid water for their development, and the high temperature of 27–28°C. The spawning ritual of the Harlequin Fish is very interesting. Before spawning the male takes up a characteristic position above the female as if trying to drive her forward by pushing her back with his mouth. The female seeks a firm leaf on a water plant (often one of the genus *Cryptocoryne*), and tests its strength by leaning on it with her belly. If it passes the test she then attaches the majority of her eggs to the underside of the leaf. More rarely the eggs are laid on the upper side of the leaf.

The Harlequin Fish is fairly vulnerable to a number of diseases caused by parasites. If, for example, they are attacked by flagellates, such as *Costia necatrix*, they die within a few hours unless treated.

302

One of the tiniest members of the Rasboras is the **Spotted** or **Pigmy Rasbora**, *Rasbora maculata* [303], which comes from the waters of the southern part of the Malayan Peninsula and Sumatra. It is only 2.5 cm (1 in) long and is found in a variety of ditches and pools. It is orange to red in colouring with dark blotches. In captivity it is most comfortable with a bed of dark peat lining the bottom of the tank. Soft water is necessary for successful spawning. Before spawning the male must be kept apart from the female for a comparatively long period. The fish requires plentiful food. If these conditions are fulfilled up to 200 eggs may be shed in a cluster of water plants at one spawning.

Meinken's Rasbora, *Rasbora meinkeni* [304], lives in the waters of Sumatra and grows to a length of 7 cm (2½ in). The species has a striking copper-yellow colouring. Another characteristic is the black longitudinal stripe which runs along the side of the body from the root of the anal fin. The **Red-striped Rasbora,** *Rasbora pauciperforata*, lives in the same waters as Meinken's Rasbora. The female [305] is distinguished from the male by her conspicuously swollen belly. From Thailand comes

303

304

Rasbora somphongsi [306]. This is a peaceable fish only 3.5 cm (1½ in) in length, which is suitable for keeping In mixed aquaria. It will feed on a variety of foodstuffs. Like Meinken's Rasbora it lays its eggs in clusters of water plants. The delicate pastel shades of this fish are only fully displayed if it is kept in a tank with a plentiful growth and a dark bed.

306

23a *Aphyosemion christyi*
23b *Aphyosemion gardneri*

24a 'Red-striped Lyretail' *(Aphyosemion lujae)* – male
24b 'Red-striped Lyretail' – female

The **Three-line Rasbora** or **Scissorstail**, *Rasbora trilineata* [307], is characterized by the extended form of its body. It is found chiefly in the waters of the Greater Sunda Islands. In nature it grows to a length of 15 cm (6 in) but in captivity it is much smaller. The Scissorstail is popular by reason of its lively antics and because it can be kept with other species. It requires soft, slightly acid water for keeping and breeding.

Rasbora leptosoma [308] lives in the streams and rivers of Sumatra. This fish is some 8 cm (3½ in) long. It has a red band running from above the eyes down to the root of the tail, with a border of gold on the upper side and scattered black markings running back from the gills. This fish has been kept in aquaria with some interruptions since 1910, although, like the remaining larger *Rasbora* species, it has acquired little popularity.

Rasbora urophthalma [309], which comes from the fresh waters of Sumatra, is only 2.5 cm (1 in) long. There is a dark stripe down the side of the body which often has a green iridescence, and a golden red upper marking. It can be bred in the smallest aquarium. The eggs are attached to the under side of leaves, or laid in a tangle of finely pinnate plants. Spawning is not restricted to a single occasion, but takes place on several consecutive days. The most suitable water temperature is 26–28°C.

The genus *Tylognathus* comes from the Indo-Australian region. It is represented by several species in Thailand. Some of them, like the 10 cm (4 in) long *Tylognathus siamensis* [310], live in large shoals in company with other cyprinid fishes and after the rainy season they swim upstream in the larger rivers.

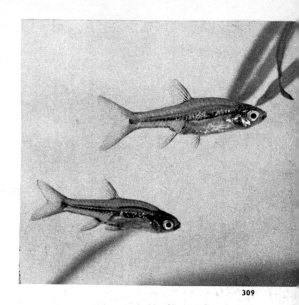

309

One of the most interesting families of southern Asian fishes is the **Gyrinocheilidae,** of which *Gyrinocheilus aymonieri* [311] is a member. This fish is common in the rivers of Thailand and measures 25 cm (10 in) in length. In captivity it is lively and requires well oxygenated water. The mouth is somewhat set back and has broad lips which have been adapted to form a sucking organ. Picture 312 shows one of these fishes attached to a stone by its mouth. On the lips there are rasp-like ridges for rubbing off the growths of algae which form the principal diet of this fish. The structure of the mouth is illustrated in picture 313. *Gyrinocheilus aymonieri* has an extra pair of gill openings through which it takes in water. The

310

311

mouth is thus left free for constant browsing. In aquaria it clings not only to stones and the glass walls, but also to the leaves of plants. Larger specimens often injure other fishes by attaching themselves to them and rubbing off their skin. The wounds then become infected, especially by fungi. It is, nevertheless, highly effective at removing algae from the walls of the aquarium.

The family **Cobitidae** (Spiny Loaches) consists of small fishes whose bodies are covered in tiny scales. The mouth is surrounded by between six and twelve barbels, and there is a large number of pharyngeal teeth symmetrically arranged. The front part of the swim-bladder is encased in a bony capsule, and in species from swifter flowing streams the back end of the swim-bladder is greatly diminished. The **Stone Loach,** *Noemacheilus barbatulus* [314], is distributed almost throughout the whole of Europe and is 8–10 cm (3–4 in) long. It is only absent from northern Scotland, Sweden, southern Spain, central and southern Italy, and Greece. Stone Loaches live near the bottom of clear, fast-flowing waters, and are usually hidden under

312

313

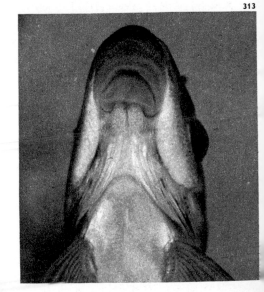

314

stones, plant roots, and other natural hiding places. They move slowly from side to side on the river bed, but do not actually cover themselves in sand. If they are surprised they shoot away like lightning and hide among the stones. They feed on the smaller animals and creatures of the river bed, which they seek out with their long, sensitive barbels [315]. A xanthic form of the Stone Loach was described by Berg in 1933 under the name *Noemacheilus barbatulus* aberr. *erythrina* [316]. It is yellow to orange in colouring with black eyes, and only isolated specimens are found.

315

316

317

The distribution of the **Weather-fish,** *Misgurnus fossilis* [317], stretches from the Seine to the Neva, and from the Danube to the Volga. It is 30 cm (12 in) long and has ten well-developed barbels [318, 319]. It lives in the still waters of muddy river meanders, and will survive in conditions which not even the most resistant of Carp or Tench will put up with. If there is a sudden change in the weather, associated with fluctuations in barometric pressure, the Weather-fish comes to

318

319

the surface and swims about excitedly. In water with a low oxygen content it gulps in air; it extracts oxygen through its intestinal mucous membrane, which has a complex lung-like system of blood vessels.

The **Spined Loach**, *Cobitis taenia* [320], is 6–12 cm ($2\frac{1}{2}$–$4\frac{1}{2}$ in) long. It has a two-pronged, retractable spine underneath each eye. The Spined Loach is found in Europe (including eastern England) and Siberia, where it prefers fast-flowing waters with a sandy or stony bed. It often buries itself in the bottom with only the head and tail poking out. Its food consists of the small creatures of the river bottom. The body of the Spined Loach is considerably compressed. The large pectoral fins of the male [321] display a peculiar basal scale, known as the Canestrini scale. This fish is easily kept in

322
323

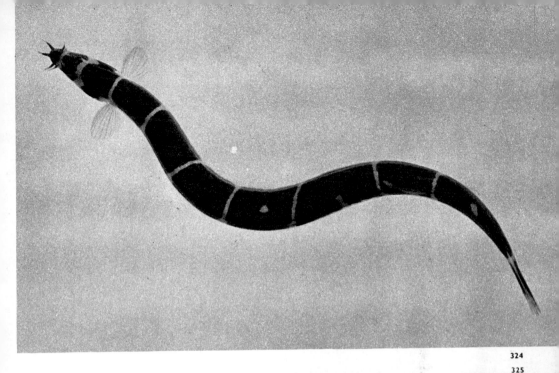

aquaria, although it is sensitive to lack of oxygen and requires clear water.

The **Half-banded Coolie Loach**, *Acanthophthalmus semicinctus* [322], which grows to a length of 8 cm (3 in), comes from Indonesia. On both sides of the body it has twelve to sixteen dark brown to black stripes which sometimes extend beyond the middle of the flank but do not pass under the body. The colouring between the bands is golden red and the underside is salmon pink. The eyes are covered with a transparent skin. A closely related species is the **Coolie Loach, Leopard Eel, Prickly Eye** or **Striped Loach**, *Acanthophthalmus kuhlii* [323], which is found in Java and Sumatra. This fish possesses three pairs of barbels and fifteen to twenty dark, regular, diagonal stripes which cross the back [324], but are interrupted on the underside [325]. The colouring is subject to variations. In some areas, for example in Sumatra, the number of diagonal stripes can be as low as twelve. Specimens with fewer stripes (twelve to fifteen) were described in 1940 by Fraser- Brunner as a separate subspecies *Acanthophthalmus kuhlii sumatranus*.

326

327

328

Acanthophthalmus myersi [326] comes from Thailand. According to Klausewitz this species is closely allied to the one just described and is distinguished from it only in colouring. It can thus be regarded rather as a subspecies of *Acanthophthalmus kuhlii*. The basic deep yellow colouring is interrupted by broad, dark brown bands, which are joined on the underneath and form rings round the body. The smallest species, only 5 cm (2 in) long, is *Acanthophthalmus robiginosus* [327], from the waters of western Java. Its nasal openings have tube-like extensions and the basic colouring is a dirty yellow-brown to red. There are up to twenty-one bands across the body. The males have larger fins. The second ray of the pectoral fin is noticeably thicker than the rest. All species of the genus *Acanthophthalmus* prefer a muddy bottom and live the life of a recluse – they are seldom seen even when kept in an aquarium. The female spawns in open water.

Acanthopsis choirorhynchus [328] lives in South-East Asia and on the Greater Sunda Islands. Its thin body has a length of about 18 cm (7 in). The line of dots along the side stretches for the complete length of the body and the colouring varies considerably, depending upon the nature of the river bed where it is caught. In the aquarium it will bury itself in fine sand. It prefers tubifex worms as food but will also take the red larvae (blood worms) of midges (Chironomidae).

Species of the genus *Botia* are more popular. These lively, restless little fishes also hide themselves if they are startled, though only for a short time. The most brightly coloured species is the **Clown Loach** or **Tiger Botia**, *Botia macracantha* [Pl. 21], from the waters of Sumatra and Borneo. In captivity it fails to reach its full length of 30 cm (12 in), nor does it breed successfully. A less striking species is *Botia horae* [329] from Thailand. This is an easily caught species, about 10 cm (4 in) long, with a greenish-brown background colouring and a light metallic iridescence. The four narrow diagonal stripes on the side of the body are only faintly marked.

330

331

Botia lecontei [330], which is only 7 cm (3 in) long, inhabits the same waters as *Botia horae*. Its basic colouring is greenish to blue-black. The fins are yellow to red.

From Pakistan comes *Botia lohachata* [331]. This fish grows to a length of 10 cm (4 in) in the aquarium. It requires clear water, rich in oxygen, at a temperature of about 25–28°C, and will feed on every kind of foodstuff including that intended for other fish.

Botia lucasbahi [332] comes from Thailand and is about 8 cm (3 in) long. It bears a strong resemblance to *Botia hymenophysa* and some authorities are of the opinion that it is in fact only a subspecies of the latter.

Botia modesta [333] has a wide area of distribution. This 10 cm (4 in) long fish is known in the Malayan Peninsula, Indo-China, and Thailand. Its colouring – grey with a light green iridescence – is not very impressive.

The smallest species is *Botia sidthimunki* [334] from Thailand. It grows to a length of only 4 cm. These fishes are wonderfully alert: nothing escapes their notice. *Botia sidthimunki* was first imported to Europe in 1959 by Klausewitz. Since then it has been regularly introduced, and even though it has not yet been successfully bred, it survives well in captivity. A slightly larger species – 6.5–8 cm (2½–3 in) long – is *Botia striata* [335]. Its body bears a row of narrow, irregularly shaped bands.

The fishes of the suborder **Siluroidei** (Catfishes) possess a scaleless body covered with little bony plates. The majority of them belong to fresh-water species; their distribution is world wide. Extinct members of the suborder are known from the Lower Tertiary. The living species are divided into some thirty families. A number of features indicate a connection with the Carps (Cyprinoidei), while others link them with the Characins (Characinoidei). Their origin is unclear.

335

Members of the family **Siluridae** are smooth skinned and possess elongated anal fins; the adipose fin is absent. They are fresh-water fishes distributed throughout Europe and Asia. The **European Catfish** or **Wels**, *Silurus glanis*, grows to a length of 5 m (16 ft) and weighs 300 kg (660 lb). It lives east of the Rhine in the rivers which flow into the Black Sea, the Caspian, and the Aral Sea and has been introduced to the British Isles. It is not found in the catchment area of the Arctic Ocean. Adult specimens feed on other fishes and indeed on any living creature which they can catch, including small mammals and birds. The Catfish is popular among anglers and can be caught in meanders and pools in the lower courses of rivers.

In Europe catches of about 50 kg (110 lb) are common [337]. The head of the Catfish [338] has six barbels, two on the upper jaw and four on the lower. Albino varieties [339] are frequent and have been introduced to the fish ponds of Europe. The Catfish is an imposing fish and to master it requires not only skill and authority, but also considerable strength. Spawning takes place in late spring or at the beginning

338

339

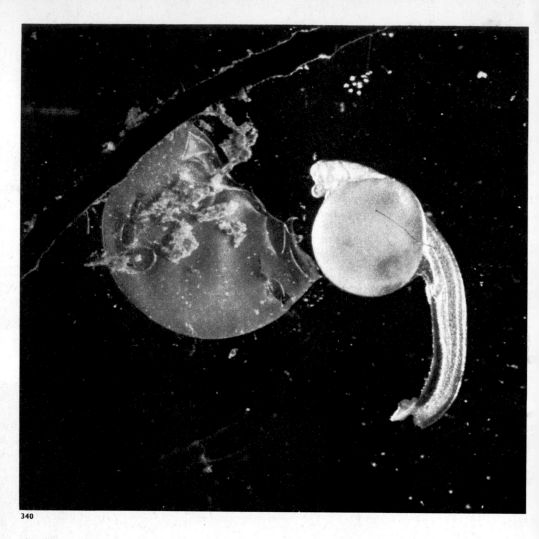

340

of summer. Catfishes choose flat spawning beds in shallow water. The male protects the eggs and the fry. As with most fishes the fry are completely helpless when they first emerge from the egg with their large yolk-sac [340]. It is several days before they discard the yolk and begin to live independently.

The **Glass Catfish,** *Kryptopterus bicirrhis* [341], lives in eastern India and the Greater Sunda Islands. The dorsal fin only develops as a single fin ray; the lower fork of the tail fin is always somewhat enlarged. The 10 cm (4 in) long body is of a glass-like transparency. When kept in aquaria they 'stand' obliquely in shoals or swim slowly around the tank.

25a Banner Lyretail *(Aphyosemion calliurum)*
25b *Aphyosemion walkeri*

26 'Burundi' *Aphyosemion*

342

A related species, the **East Indies Glass Catfish,** *Kryptopterus macrocephalus* [342], comes from Indonesia. It has a very thin, compressed body which is less transparent than that of the Glass Catfish and has a yellow-green or grey colouring; when light falls on the body it has a blue iridescence. The anal fin is connected to the tail fin by a fine membrane.

Tropical waters are always yielding new, previously unknown fishes. Picture 343 shows a newly impor-

ted Catfish not previously described. At first sight it would appear to belong to the genus *Kryptopterus*.

Members of the family **Plotosidae** are typically salt-water Catfishes. These fishes come from the Pacific and Indian oceans. *Plotosus arab* carries an impressive series of longitudinal stripes throughout its life, whereas the adult specimens are usually one colour only. *Plotosus lineatus* [344], is

343

about 5–10 cm (2–4 in) long although it has been known to reach a length of 80 cm (32 in). It is chiefly found on coral reefs and in estuaries. *Plotosus anguillaris* is feared by both swimmers and other fishes owing to its poison glands, which are situated near the dorsal fin and pectoral fins. Nevertheless, its flesh is prized in many places as a delicacy requiring careful preparation. When hunting for food it always swims in dense shoals. If kept in captivity it seeks out a variety of hiding places. This fish is fastidious about salinity, although it will survive transfer into brackish or fresh water.

The family **Bagridae** also belongs to the suborder Siluroidei. A characteristic of these Catfishes is the adipose fin between the dorsal and tail fins.

Auchenoglanis occidentalis [345] has a wide distribution in African fresh water. This Catfish lives in the lower course of the Nile, in the Senegal river, and in the Congo and is up to 50 cm (20 in) long. These creatures must be kept in isolation in the aquarium since they are predators and will snap at everything that moves. Their colouring is subject to great variation, from a uniform brown to violet, and specimens may even be found with a dark hatching on a light ground.

Leiocassis siamensis [346], with a length of 17 cm (6½ in), comes from Thailand. The torpedo-shaped body of this fish is dorsiventrally compressed. It has four pairs of short barbels. The under part [347] is light brown to yellow in colouring and the sides are coffee-brown, dark blue or grey-blue with four irregularly placed yellowish stripes. It is imported from time to time and is quite popular. *Leiocassis brashnikowi* [348] is a native of the Amur river. This fish is some 22 cm (8½ in) long. The light yellow colouring of the adult is flecked with dark spots.

The Catfishes of the family **Ictaluridae** are chiefly North American. They have tadpole-like bodies with a large broad head, four pairs of barbels, and a well-developed adipose fin.

The **Brown Bullhead,** *Ictalurus nebulosus* [349], comes from Indiana, Florida and the eastern states of the USA. It is 40 cm (16 in) long and up to 2 kg (4½ lb) in weight. It was introduced to Europe during the last century and it is found today in the Danube, the Elbe, and other European river systems, although there is evidence to suggest that the species introduced to Europe was *Ictalurus melas*. Dr Breder in the USA has been able to observe spawning in the aquarium. In nature it hollows out shallow depressions in which to spawn. The eggs and fry are protected by the male. The Brown Bullhead feeds principally on the fauna of the river bed. In the aquarium, however, it is dangerous to other fishes since it requires a great deal of space and is ruthless in maintaining its territory at the expense of other fishes.

The family **Schilbeidae** is found in the waters of Asia and Africa. In some – but not all – species an adipose fin is present. The long anal fin and other features are reminiscent of members of the family Siluridae. The pectoral fins are equipped with a strong spine.

The genus *Pangasius*, which belongs to this family, occurs throughout the whole Indo-Malayan region. Some species are up to 50 cm (20 in) long.

349

350

351

232

The most common species is *Pangasius sutchi* [350], which has been imported and is popular among aquarists. This species was first caught in Menan, Chao Phya, and Bangkok and was described in 1937 by Fowler. The two long barbels on the lower jaw reach as far as the centre of the eye. It has not yet been successfully reared in captivity.

The family **Clariidae** consists of long-bodied Catfishes with broad heads and protruding mouths set at an angle. They have four pairs of barbels. The typical feature of this family is the auxiliary air-breathing organs for taking in additional oxygen. These organs either consist of two sacs situated between the gill opening down both sides of the spine or are much-branched structures lying behind the gills. Owing to their ability to breathe air the Clariidae are able to survive in completely stagnant waters lacking in oxygen and even to leave the water altogether. Occasionally *Heteropneustes fossilis* [351] is kept in aquaria. This fish comes from Ceylon, eastern India, Burma, and South Vietnam, and grows to a length of up to 70 cm (28 in). In the male the spines of the dorsal and pectoral fins are equipped with poison glands. A wound from one of these spines can induce temporary or permanent paralysis of the extremities. Fishermen are wary of this Catfish and if they find one in their net they take the precaution of cutting the fish out together with a section of the net.

The family **Pimelodidae** contains a large number of Central and South American species. They have three pairs of very long barbels and the dorsal

fin is close to the head. The anal fin is short and the adipose fin takes various forms. The jaws are equipped with teeth. This family consists generally of small fishes which are diverse in appearance.

Pimelodella gracilis [352] inhabits the Orinoco and the Amazon rivers. It is 17 cm (6½ in) long. Its anal fin is rounded and the tail fin is deeply indented with a slightly larger upper fork. On the upper jaw there is a pair of very long barbels [353]; both pairs of barbels on the lower jaw are much shorter. The barbels are dark on the upper side and silvery-white on the lower.

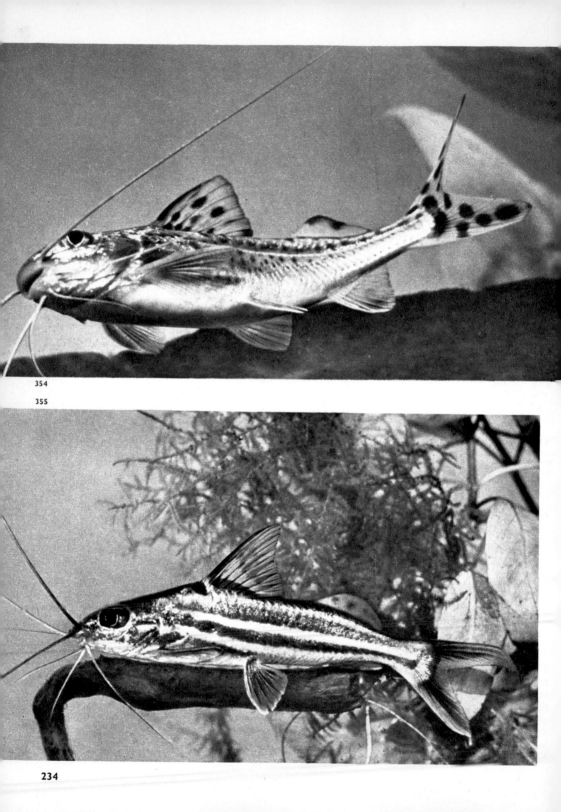

354

355

356

Other species of the genus *Pimelodella* are occasionally introduced, for example the one known to aquarists under the name *Pimelodella picta* [354]. Precise classification is often hindered by the fact that exact information about the place of origin is not always available or is deliberately suppressed by the importer. For this reason it is not possible to give any definite information about the specimen in picture 355. Nevertheless, from its general appearance, there is no doubt that it belongs to the genus *Pimelodella*.

Members of the family **Mochocidae** are native to African waters south of the Sahara. They have an adipose fin, a rounded back, and three pairs of barbels. The Mochocidae are exclusively crepuscular (halflight) fishes which often congregate in large shoals. They are found both in flowing waters and in still lagoons.

Synodontis melanostictus [356] lives in the Zambezi and in lakes Tanganyika, Bangwulu, and Mweru. Its maximum length is 32 cm (13 in). The shoulder flaps form a distinctive spiked ruff. The upper fork of the tail fin is generally larger than the lower. The body is light to dark brown with many black blotches, while the under part is lighter. The barbels are fringed and their shape can be clearly seen in picture 357. This species feeds principally on the fauna of the river or lake bed and prefers shady aquaria.

357

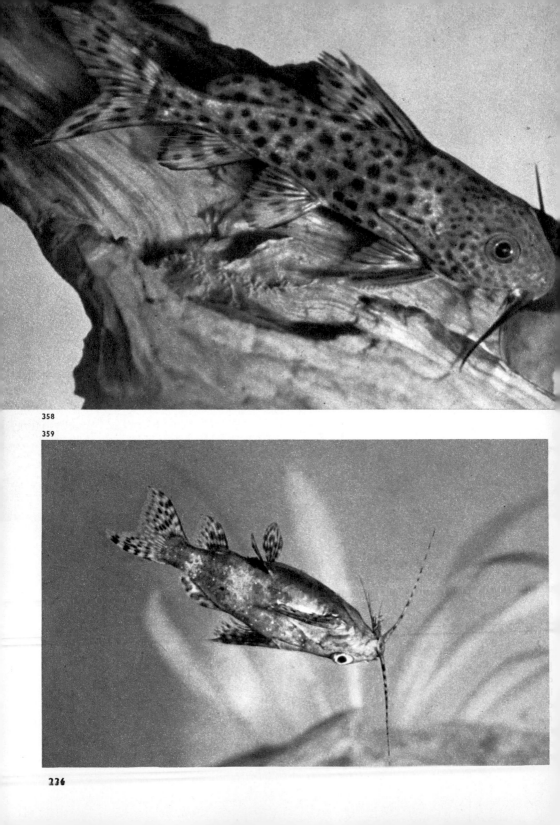

358

359

Synodontis nigrita [358] lives in the White Nile, Senegal, Niger, and Gambia rivers. It is about 17 cm (6½ in) in length. The front spine of the dorsal fin is smooth. The young are coffee-brown in colour and covered with a large number of black spots which sometimes coalesce to form cross stripes. The adults are grey-green in colour.

The **Upside-down Catfish,** *Synodontis nigriventris* [359], is only 6 cm (2½ in) long and is found in the central Congo region. The belly of this little fish is dark brown to black while the back is lighter in colour. The females are more resilient than the males. In the aquarium the Upside-down Catfish is an undemanding creature with the interesting and most unusual habit of swimming upside-down near the surface of the water. It feeds on live animals and also on algae. These fishes lay their eggs in hidden and well-protected places: a small flowerpot is sufficient for this purpose.

In the Nile, the Senegal, Lake Chad and elsewhere in Africa, lives *Synodontis schall* [360]. Its length is in the order of 40 cm (16 in) and its colouring is not striking. The adults of this species are an almost uniform dark grey or brown with a light or even white belly. Immature specimens are olive-brown, marbled in a darker shade of brown. *Synodontis schall* feeds mainly on insects which fall on to the surface of the water; it swims up to the surface with belly uppermost to catch them. The ancient Egyptians were familiar with this fish and some of their paintings of it have survived to the present day.

361

The family **Malapteruridae** contains the genus *Malapterurus* represented by a single species, the **Electric Catfish**, *Malapterurus electricus* [361]. It is an inhabitant of tropical Africa and has six barbels. The dorsal fin is missing and has been replaced by a well-developed adipose fin set right at the tail of the body. The anal fin is short, the eyes are remarkably small and the gills are narrow. The electric organs are found in the connective tissue under the thick skin of the belly. Little is known about the biology of the Electric Catfish. The Arab fishermen of the Nile claim that the fish keeps its eggs and the newly emerged young in its mouth, but this has not been scientifically confirmed.

The family **Callichthyidae** (Mailed Catfishes) is native to the waters of South America. Its members are distinguished by a short high forehead which is covered with two rows of bony plates arranged herringbone fashion. These creatures first appear

among fossils of the Upper Tertiary. A large number of small aquarium species, often extremely brightly coloured, belong to this family.

The **Bronze Corydoras**, *Corydoras aeneus* [363], which grows to a length of 7 cm (2½ in), lives in the waters of Venezuela and Trinidad and is also found southwards as far as the River Plate. Its colouring is a uniform yellow to pinkish-brown with a strong metallic sheen. The flanks of the body often have a greenish or copper-coloured iridescence, which in strong sunlight is almost golden.

The **Arched Corydoras**, *Corydoras arcuatus* [362], comes from the neighbourhood of the city of Teffé on the Amazon. It is about 5 cm (2 in) in length. Stretching from the mouth, over the eye and down the back there is a broad, dark, arched band which tapers off towards the tail, although it extends into the lower fork of the tail fin. This species lives and feeds on the bottom.

362

363

364

365

The **Dwarf** or **Pigmy Corydoras**, *Corydoras pygmaeus* [364], inhabits the region of Villa Bella on the Amazon. It is only 3 cm (1 in) long and is distinguished from other Corydoras by its habit of ranging across the aquarium in shoals. Only when it is startled by sudden alterations in the lighting or some other shock does it briefly seek a hiding place on the bottom.

The **Leopard Corydoras**, *Corydoras julii* [365], is found in the smallest tributaries of the lower course of the Amazon and is about 6 cm (2½ in) in length. Its colouring is highly variable. A very common colour variant was described by Myers in 1933 under the name *Corydoras leopardus*. According to Myers' description the colouring is influenced by age and by the size of the body. In picture 366 a young specimen about 3 cm (1 in) long is shown.

The smaller tributaries of the Amazon above its confluence with the Negro river form the home of **Myers' Corydoras**, *Corydoras myersi* [367]. This species, which is about 6 cm (2½ in) long, has lovely colouring. A broad, dark band stretches across a bright orange-red ground from the dorsal fin down to the tail. The gill covers and part of the flanks have a green iridescence. It is not difficult to keep in aquaria although it has rarely been successfully bred.

The **Dwarf** or **Rabaut's Corydoras**, *Corydoras rabauti* [368], comes from the area of the junction of the Negro and Amazon rivers. This fish is frequently confused with the last mentioned species, from which it is only distinguished by its size – it is just 3 cm (1 in) long – and its bright red, sometimes purple tinged, colouring. This is a lively little fish and when it feels completely at home it swims about the tank, only seeking shelter near the bottom when it is startled or looking for food. The species has only occasionally been imported and has almost never been bred in captivity.

The most popular member of the genus *Corydoras* is the **Peppered Corydoras**, *Corydoras paleatus* [369]. This species comes from south-east Brazil

366

367

and from the river Plate basin. It has been kept in Europe since 1878, when Carbonnier first successfully bred it in Paris. The males are smaller than the females and are distinguished by a permanently erect dorsal fin. There is also a very common and fecund albino form [370] which has the red eyes typical of albinos.

Corydoras elegans [371] is a native of the central course of the Amazon. This fish is at most 6 cm

(2½ in) long and its body has a striking, marbled pattern. The gill covers are a wonderful, iridescent turqoise in colour and the dorsal fin is marked with a dark patch.

Corydoras punctatus [372] comes from the waters of the Orinoco, the Essequibo, and the Amazon. In nature this species grows to a length of 6 cm (2½ in). Its basic colouring is a light, smoky or yellowish grey, with many rows of dark flecks.

368

27   Banded Epiplatys *(Epiplatys fasciolatus)*

28 *Epiplatys annulatus*

The place of origin of the **Reticulated Corydoras,** *Corydoras reticulatus* [373], is not known exactly but it is said to come from the Amazon near Monte Alegre. The dorsal fin has a number of dark spots on a dark ground. In young specimens the dorsal fin exhibits a dark patch with a light border. The basic colouring consists of a shimmering, greenish red with darker, or even black, hatching.

Corydoras caudimaculatus [374] lives in the Guaporé river on the border of Brazil and Bolivia. Its length is about 5 cm (2 in). Slightly acid water is the best medium for *Corydoras caudimaculatus*. It usually gets its food from the river bed. The body is covered all over in small blotches and there is a characteristic, large, black patch at the root of the tail fin.

370

371

372

373

Corydoras macropterus [375] grows to a length of 7 cm (3 in) and lives in the waters of southern Brazil. It has bristles on its cheeks. The basic colouring is grey-brown with black markings, while the dorsal and anal fins have rows of spots: the spine of the dorsal fin is black. A water temperature of 18–21°C is necessary for this species to be successfully kept.

The species *Brochis coeruleus* [376] comes from the neighbourhood of Iquitos on the upper Amazon. It is approximately 7 cm (3 in) long and its high body is flat-sided. The dorsal fin is longer than that of the preceding species. The body is coloured an iridescent emerald green, while the under-

neath is ochre. *Brochis coeruleus* is an attractive fish but unfortunately it is seldom imported and somewhat difficult to keep.

The **Cascadura,** *Hoplosternum thoracatum* [377], comes from the Amazon basin and from Guyana and Trinidad. It is 20 cm (8 in) long and its colouring varies from olive-brown to grey. The whole body, including the fins and the belly, is covered in large and small specks [378]. The Cascadura builds a bubble nest just below the water's surface on the underneath of a large leaf. The female lays her eggs in the nest which is guarded by the male as are the fry, which emerge from the eggs some four days after fertilization.

376

The **Loricariidae** (Armoured Catfishes) are confined to the northern and central parts of South America. They live principally in small, fast-flowing mountain streams. The bodies are typically covered with a thick armour coat and all the fins except for the tail fin have a strong, sharp spine. The mouth is set back on the underneath of the head and has broad lips enabling it to serve as a sucking organ, by means of which the fish attaches itself to stones or plant roots, on the bottom. *Loricaria filamentosa* [379] comes from the Magdalena river. Its normal length of 25 cm (10 in) is never achieved by specimens kept in captivity. It is characterized by a long thin body. The uppermost ray of the tail fin is greatly extended. The male can easily be distinguished from the female by examina-

tion of the dark bristles covering the upper side of its pectoral fin. The female lays large orange-coloured eggs in recesses and holes, between stones or, in the aquarium, in an artificially constructed tube. The male guards the eggs and frees the young from the egg membrane.

Otocinclus maculipinnis [380] is only 4 cm (1½ in) long. This species is a native of the river Plate and its tributaries. It is likewise a member of the family Loricariidae and bears a close resemblance to the genus *Corydoras*, particularly in its courtship display. The eggs are small and are attached to water plants and to the wall of the aquarium. The young hatch within two or three days at temperatures above 20°C. After a further two or three days they swim freely and begin to search for food. The adult fishes make themselves useful by cleaning

algae off the water plants and glass walls of the aquarium.

The **Blue-chin Xenocara,** *Xenocara dolichoptera,* is a native of the Amazon and of Guyana. This fish is 13 cm (5 in) long. The front of its head is almost always equipped with long, upright, forked tentacles [381], which are shorter and thinner in the female. Spawning occurs in recesses which the fish itself builds under stones or pieces of wood. The male takes intensive care of the spawn. In the aquarium the Blue-chin Xenocara makes no particular demands with regard to the composition of the water: it is easy to keep.

Hancock's Amblydoras, *Amblydoras hancocki* [382], belongs to the family **Doradidae** (Thorny Catfishes). These are heavily armoured catfishes

with four bony plates, equipped with thorns and little teeth above, along each side [383].

Seen from above the body looks extremely short. The pectoral fins are equipped with a powerful spine, and there is a small adipose fin. The Thorny Catfishes are found right up the Amazon to its sources in Peru and also in the rivers of Bolivia and Guyana. They are also known as Talking Catfishes for they make a growling or grunting noise which is produced by movement of the pectoral fin. The mechanism by which this noise is produced is not yet fully understood. The females lay their eggs in a nest built of vegetable matter, and both parents take care of the spawn. They have not yet been successfully reared in the aquarium. They are hardy fishes and can withstand temporary exposure to low temperatures.

382

383

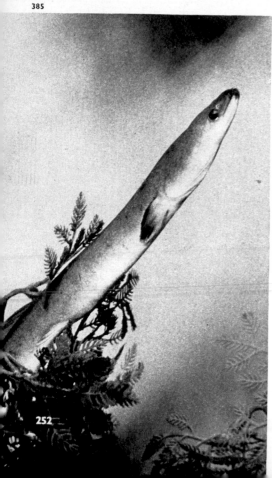

The distinguishing feature of the Eels, order **Anguilliformes**, is a long snake-like body: they possess up to 260 vertebrae. The scales are either rudimentary or absent altogether. The order contains some twenty-five families, of which the first, **Anguillidae**, consists of only one genus, *Anguilla*, with several species distributed throughout the Atlantic, Indian, and Pacific oceans. They are not found on the South American coasts of the Pacific. The **European Eel** (*Anguilla anguilla*), the **American Eel** (*Anguilla rostrata*), and, in the Pacific, the **Japanese Eel**, *Anguilla japonica* [385], occur in the northern hemisphere. The home of *Anguilla anguilla* is along the coasts of Europe. Smaller specimens are easy to keep in aquaria [384], but adults weigh up to 7 kg (15 lb). The Eel has been highly valued by man from the beginning of history, and is frequently kept in fish ponds. If conditions in one stretch of water are not to the liking of the Eel it may travel considerable distances to another place and will not hesitate to go overland [386]. Much is still unknown about the reproduction of the Eel, but the broad outlines are known. The sexually maturing Eels swim down river and out to sea. Spawning is believed to take place in the Sargasso Sea near the Bermudas at the enormous depth of about 7,000 m (23,000 ft). After spawning the adults die. The smallest fry that have ever been found are only 7–15 mm (0.3–0.6 in) in size. They remain at a depth of about 180–200 m (580–650 ft), where the temperature is in the region of 20°C,

29 *Nothobranchius melanospilus*

30　Rachov's Nothobranchius *(Nothobranchius taeniopygus)*

31 Guppy (*Poecilia reticulata*)

32a 'Meri-gold Platy' (variety of *Xiphophorus variatus*)
32b Platy *(Xiphophorus maculatus)*

growing rapidly, so that in the first year they reach a length of 2.5 cm (1 in).

In the course of the next two years they make

their way back to the coasts of Europe, swimming close to the surface and making use of the North Atlantic Drift. This is known as a 'passive migra-

388

tion'. At first they have the shape of a willow leaf, and are known as Leptocephalus since they were once thought to be a distinct species, but they soon take on the familiar eel shape of the elver.

389

Eels penetrate far up streams and rivers, but a substantial proportion of them stay in inshore waters and estuaries. It was at one time claimed that only females were found in fresh water, where they may live for between nine and twelve years, but this is not always the case. Eels are of considerable economic importance.

The Morays or Moray Eels, members of the family **Muraenidae**, have a scaleless body which is usually brightly coloured. The tail is very long, the unpaired fins are atrophied, and the pectoral fins are lacking entirely. More than 100 species are known. Morays are for the most part aggressive even without provocation and the larger species up to 2.5 m (8 ft) long, are counted among the most dangerous creatures of tropical seas. Their blood serum is poisonous and induces disintegration of the blood corpuscles of mammals. However when they are cooked the poison is destroyed once the temperature exceeds 75°C. Some Morays have further poison glands situated near the teeth. The genus *Muraena* is found in tropical and subtropical seas. A group of **Common Morays** *Muraena helena*, is shown in picture 388. Their nostrils open at the end of a tube-like process [389]. Common Morays are found in the Mediterranean and the eastern Atlantic, where they of

rare occasions extend as far north as the southern coasts of England. They grow to a length of up to 120 cm (47 in) and their flesh was regarded as a great delicacy by the ancient Romans, who kept them in special ponds (piscinae).

The **Clouded Moray,** *Echidna nebulosa* [390], lives in the coral reefs of the Indo-Pacific area. The irises of its eyes and the tip of its tail are orange coloured and there are small, orange patches in the star-like black marks along the side of the body. The Clouded Moray is about 60 cm (24 in) long.

Echidna delicatula [391] is a brownish colour with fine irregular hatching. The dorsal fin extends in front of the gills.

The **Congridae** (Conger Eels) have scaleless bodies and broad mouths. The pectoral and the unpaired fins are well developed. The dorsal fin

393

begins immediately behind the head above the pectoral fins. These are oceanic Eels living in the Atlantic, Indian, and Pacific oceans. *Conger conger* [392] lives in the Atlantic and Mediterranean. This Eel is 2–3 m (6–10 ft) long and up to 65 kg (140 lb) in weight. Little is known of its reproductive biology or of its migratory patterns, but it is believed to breed in deep water over the continental shelf.

The members of the order **Beloniformes** (Gars) possess an extremely elongated body, cycloid scales, spineless fins, a lateral line along the lower half of the body, and pectoral fins placed high on the sides. Their bones are green in colour. Extinct forms are known from the Eocene. In recent times the majority of Beloniformes live in the salt waters along the coasts of the Pacific Ocean. The original forms were littoral in their habits and pelagic forms are believed to have only developed later on. The most familiar member of the family **Belonidae** is the **Garfish** or **Garpike**, *Belone*

bellone, seen in picture 393 in the middle of a shoal of sardines. It grows to a length of 90 cm (36 in) but weighs less than 1 kg (2 lb). In the Black Sea some 500 tons of Garpike are caught annually. They feed on molluscs and small fishes. Their flesh has an excellent taste despite the green bones.

The Halfbeaks (family **Hemirhamphidae**) are frequently kept in aquaria, and the most familiar of them is undoubtedly the '**Wrestling Halfbeak**', *Dermogenys pusillus* [394]. This fish comes from the waters of Thailand, the Malayan Peninsula, and the Greater Sunda Islands. It lives in brackish and fresh water. The male grows to a length of 6 cm (2½ in) and the female to 7 cm (3 in). *Dermogenys pusillus* must be fed with land insects (fruit flies, mosquitoes, and the larvae of almost any species) and a plentiful supply of water fleas. It is not easy to keep this species, for the females miscarry if they are not properly fed. The fry are comparatively large – about 1 cm (½ in). The lower jaw only becomes extended as the fish grows older.

The family **Exocoetidae** contains the Flying Fishes which live in the tropical zones of the Atlantic, Pacific, and Indian oceans. They are adapted to life in the surface waters of the ocean and possess the ability to glide for some distance above the waves. The pectoral fins are broad and long and strutted throughout their whole length with strong fin rays. The lower lobe of the tail fin is very well developed. The period of 'flight' lasts up to ten seconds and distances of over 100 m (325 ft) are sometimes covered. Picture 395 shows an **Atlantic Flying Fish,** *Exocoetus volitans.*

396

The **Gadiformes** (Codfishes) possess an elaborate, well developed swim-bladder which is not connected with the intestinal tract. The ventral fins are situated in front of the pectoral fins. There are no spiny fin rays. The Gadiformes are pelagic and are found in the colder oceans of both hemispheres. They are of enormous economic importance forming an important part of the fishes caught in temperate seas [398]. Many familiar food fishes are numbered among this order including **Ling, Whiting, Saithe** and **Hake,** *Merluccius merluccius* [399], while smaller but abundant species are caught and processed into fish meal.

The most familiar species in the family **Gadidae** is almost certainly the **Cod** or **Codling,** *Gadus morhua* [396], which grows to a length of 150 cm (60 in) and weighs up to 40 kg (88 lb). It lives in the northern Atlantic along the coasts of both Europe and America and is also present in the Baltic and White Seas. There is a large number of local populations. Spawning takes place between January and March; the eggs (1.5–10 million in a single spawning) are pelagic.

Adult specimens of the **Haddock,** *Melanogrammus aeglefinus* [397], have a black mark on the sides

397

401

above the pectoral fins. The range of this fish extends from the eastern part of the Barents Sea as far south as the Bay of Biscay, and it is found off the Atlantic coast of America. The Haddock is the most economically important fish of the Atlantic Ocean after the Cod. In 1968 over 360,000 tons were caught in the north-east Atlantic area, the greater part of it in the neighbourhood of Iceland, the Faroes, and the North Sea. The Haddock grows to about 1 m (3 ft) long and weighs up to 12 kg (26 lb). Haddock are prepared for distribution in a wide variety of ways, the simplest being to put them on ice. Drying is carried out on a large scale in Iceland. Sometimes the skin is removed and the fish is boned, packed, and deep-frozen.

These deep-frozen, prepacked, fillets of Haddock are marketed throughout the world.

The only member of the Gadiformes which lives in fresh water is the **Burbot**, *Lota lota*. It prefers cool waters and occurs in rivers and lakes of Europe and North America. The Burbot is rare in England and absent from western France and Norway. It is occasionally angled for [401], usually during the winter when it spawns. The Burbot may be 1 m (3 ft) long and up to 16 kg (35 lb) in weight. The fish does not become mature until the third year of life. It is a bronze-coloured fish with delicately flavoured, rather fatty meat. Burbots have a barbel in the middle of the lower jaw [400].

402

The order **Gasterosteiformes** consists of small fishes with several erectile spines in front of the dorsal fin. The abdominal fins have a strong, sharp spine and between one and three softer rays. The Sticklebacks, family **Gasterosteidae,** comprise five genera. Three of these genera are exclusively salt-water dwellers while *Gasterosteus* and *Pungitius* are fresh-water fishes, although both may be found in brackish, estuarine water and the former even in the sea. The **Three-spined Stickleback,** *Gasterosteus aculeatus* [402], lives along the coasts of Europe from the Black Sea to Novaya Zemlya, the western Pacific coast from the Bering Straits to Korea, and the coasts of North America as far south as California. It may be up to 10 cm (4 in) long and has a variable number of spines on the dorsal fin, and a variable number of bony plates covering its body. During the mating season the males are especially brightly coloured. They build nests from bits of plant matter in which the female lays between 90 and 250 eggs. The eggs and the emerging young are protected by the male. The

403

Three-spined Stickleback is not only frequently kept by aquarists but has also been introduced to many places where it has subsequently continued to live and reproduce successfully.

The **Ten-spined Stickleback,** *Pungitius pungitius* [403] is a related species with a similar range of distribution to that of the Three-spined Stickleback. The nest is built by the male among water plants and is rather more impressive in this species. This Stickleback is at most 9 cm (3½ in) long.

The order of **Syngnathiformes** contains a number of families, the most familiar of which is the **Syngnathidae** (Pipefishes). They possess a character-istic body shape and the dorsal fin is either spineless or absent. The two nasal openings are at the side of the head. The genus *Syngnathus* is known from fossils of the Lower Eocene. The male possesses a brood pouch on his belly which is used to keep the eggs and the fry while they develop. The pouch is protected by folds of skin and a bony plate. The body of the Pipefish is very thin and is hexagonal in section. More than fifty species are known, distributed throughout all the seas of the world.

The colouring of the **Great Pipefish,** *Syngnathus acus* [404] varies from grey through various depths of red to black. It is 30 cm (12 in) long. It is common in shallow coastal waters of northern Europe.

405

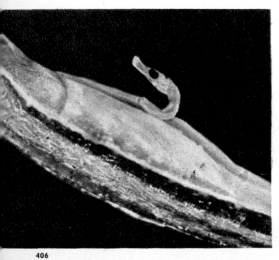

406

407

The head with sucking mouth in picture 405 is that of a **Deep-snouted** or **Broad-nosed Pipe-fish,** *Syngnathus typhle.* This species lives in the coastal waters of Europe and is up to 40 cm (16 in) long. The underside of a male is shown with a young Pipefish peeping out of the pocket [406].

The **Aulostomidae** (Trumpet Fishes) are covered with ctenoid scales. There are several thin and isolated spines along the back in front of the dorsal fin. The genus *Aulostomus* is represented by a number of species in the tropical regions of the Pacific and Atlantic oceans. *Aulostomus maculatus* [407], from the coast of Cuba, is singularly well adapted to its environment: its tube-shaped, suctorial mouth is highly effective for catching small fishes.

The Shrimpfishes, family **Centriscidae,** which come from the Pacific and Indian Oceans, have an entirely scaleless body protected by an outer armour of bone. The short tail appears as a direct extension of the dorsal fin, which forms the end of the body. Razorfishes swim with their heads pointing directly downwards [408], although they will happily adopt the reverse posture. When threatened they turn their razor thin bodies towards the intruder and become difficult to spot.

The **Common Shrimpfish** or **Razorfish,** *Aeoliscus strigatus,* is shown in picture 408: it lives in small shoals.

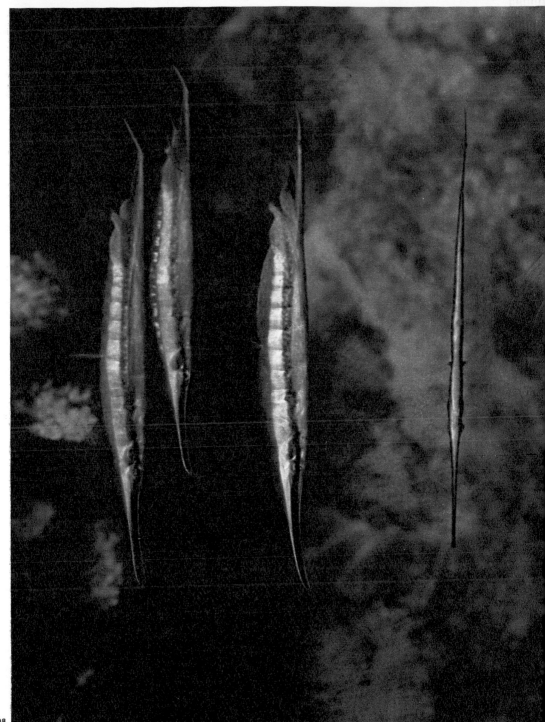

The Seahorses belong to the family **Hippocampi-dae** which is closely related to the Shrimpfishes. The body is flattened laterally and the belly narrows towards the head forming a neck. Seahorses swim in an upright position with the head pointing forwards. They have no tail fins, but use their tails to attach themselves to plants. The males have a broad pouch. Some Seahorses grow to a length of 15 cm (6 in). Some species can be kept by experienced aquarists, for example the **Short-nosed Seahorses,** *Hippocampus brevirostris* [409], and the **Common Seahorse,** *Hippocampus guttulatus* [410]. Their reproductive cycle has been observed many times in the aquarium although it has not yet proved possible to raise the young to full adulthood after they leave the pouch of the male. The food requirements for normal healthy growth are as yet unknown.

409

The order **Cyprinodontiformes** (Tooth-carps) consists of small fishes with a protrusible mouth in which the bones of the jaw are bordered with small teeth. There are no hard fin rays nor any lateral lines. The pectoral fins are inserted on the side of the body and their bases are perpendicular to the long axis. Fossil species are known from the Oligocene. A whole series of families belongs to this order. The Egg-laying Tooth-carps, **Cyprinodontidae**, live in the fresh waters of South America, Africa, southern Europe, and southern Asia. Many have been introduced to foreign countries in order to control mosquito larvae

and some of them are very popular acquisitions for the aquarium, not least because of their bright, gay colouring. Some species are able to survive the dry season in the egg although the adults die.

The inconspicuously coloured *Aphanius fasciatus* [411] lives in brackish water around the Mediterranean. It grows to a length of about 6 cm (2½ in). It would be easy to keep in the aquarium if only the adults did not have powerful cannibalistic tendencies. Even in the thickest tangle of plants they take a very short time to seek out the spawn. It is essential to separate eggs from parents.

412

413

The **Blue Panchax**, *Aplocheilus lineatus*, comes from western India and Ceylon. It is 10 cm (4 in) long. Picture 412 shows a male; it is more slender than the female and more brightly coloured. This fish is undemanding about the composition of the water. It lays its eggs in a tangle of fine-leafed water plants near the bottom or immediately underneath the surface. The Blue Panchax prefers clear warm water at a temperature of 23–25°C. The act of spawning sometimes extends over several consecutive days. The young emerge after about twelve to fifteen days depending on the water temperature and are best reared on living plank-ton. Adult specimens, especially the older creatures, are aggressive and have been known to consume an adult female Zebra Danio; they are therefore not suitable for keeping in mixed aquaria. The effect of the males in their full iridescent coloration before mating is fascinating. Two such males are seen in picture 413, while the foreground of picture 414 shows a female with the characteristic vertical stripes on the side of her body. The Blue Panchax was first imported to Europe in 1909 and there is still a great deal of interest in this fish today. A number of varieties has arisen as a result of selective breeding.

414

415

416

The extensive genus *Aphyosemion*, also of the family Cyprinodontidae, is very popular among aquarists. It is an exclusive African genus, frequently occurring in small bodies of water such as rain ponds and drainage ditches. The delta of the Ogooué in Gabon is the home of the brightly coloured **Cape Lopez Lyretail**, *Aphyosemion australe* [415], which is less than 6 cm (2½ in) in length. The gay colouring of the male is shown in colour plate 22a. The Cape Lopez Lyretail requires extremely soft water if it is to reproduce successfully. It spawns in fine-leafed water plants, such as the Water Bladderwort, *Utricularia* [416], or in aquatic moss of the genus *Fontinalis*. The fry emerge after fourteen to sixteen days at a temperature of 26°C.

Aphyosemion gulare [417] grows to a length of 8–12 cm (3–4½ in). The homeland of this fish is Nigeria. It is a short-lived species and rarely survives for more than one year. However, it is not difficult to keep. The most suitable water temperature is 22–23°C when spawning is intensive. The temperature should be raised to 26–28°C in order to rear the young without unnecessary losses.

The **Red Lyretail**, *Aphyosemion bivittatum* [418], comes from Cameroon and the Niger delta. It grows to a length of about 6 cm (2½ in) and is one of the Cyprinodontid species which are distinguished by extreme variations in colouring and

419

fin shape. Specimens are known with both short and long fins and with yellow, red, or violet as their basic colouring. The eggs are laid in thickets of water plants and the young emerge after fifteen to twenty days.

The basic colouring of Aphyosemion christyi (or Aphyosemion cognatum), which comes from the Congo, is an orange-red (Pl. 23a). This fish is 5 cm (2 in) in length. It spawns in spring, preferably near the surface of the water. The young emerge after twelve to sixteen days and are very dark in colouring at first.

Aphyosemion cinnamomeum [419] inhabits clear streams and peat ponds of the African jungle. It was first imported in 1962. The characteristic colouring of the male does not develop until the end of the first year of life, although other sexual distinguishing features are present at four to five months. Spawning takes place near the bottom in a layer of peat.

The exact place of origin of the **Plumed Lyretail** Aphyosemion filamentosum, is not known although it has been suggested that it comes from Togo. It grows to a length of about 4.5 cm (2 in) in the aquarium and lives for several years. The Plumed Lyretail is a beautiful, lively, little fish which keeps to the middle of the tank. There are numerous variations in form and colouring. Before spawning the males often take up a characteristic threat posture [420]. Spawning takes place over sand, peat or low-growing vegetation. The fry hatch from the eggs after upwards of fourteen days. Picture 421 shows a half-grown male.

Aphyosemion gardneri [422] lives in tropical West Africa and has often been wrongly identified by aquarists as Aphyosemion calliurum calliurum (the Red-chinned Lyretail). A number of colour variations are known, among which the most typical has been wrongly regarded as a subspecies (Aphyosemion calliurum ahli) [423, Pl. 23b]. This variety has a striking yellow border to the dorsal

422

anal, and tail fins. *Aphyosemion gardneri* prefers to spawn on gravel [424]. The male has laid his dorsal fin over the back of the female.

Aphyosemion gardneri can be crossed with the Cape Lopez Lyretail and picture 425 shows the hybrid resulting from such a cross. In some male hybrids the dorsal, tail and anal fins form one continuous unit [426], giving the fish a bizarre appearance with little resemblance to either of the parents.

The tropical parts of West Africa are inhabited by a number of further species of the genus *Aphyo-*

423

semion of which the most colourful are the '**Red-striped Lyretail**' *Aphyosemion lujae* (syn. *Aphyosemion striatum*) [Pl. 24], *Aphyosemion walkeri* [Pl. 25b], the **Banner Lyretail** *Aphyosemion calliurum* [Pl. 25a], and a species which has not yet been satisfactorily classified, known as the '**Burundi' Aphyosemion** [Pl. 26].

Fundulosoma thierryi [427] is a comparatively small species, measuring only 4 cm (1½ in). It lives in a variety of marshy waters and pools in Ghana – particularly in the neighbourhood of Takoradi – and in Nigeria. If this species is to be kept it requires soft, slightly acid water. In nature the eggs, like those of a number of other *Aphyosemion* species,

279

undergo a period of drying-out. However, in the aquarium they can remain in a shallow basin of water until the emergence of the fry.

The **Golden Pheasant**, *Roloffia occidentalis* [428] – formerly known as *Aphyosemion sjoestedti* – has been kept in aquaria since 1909. It grows to a length of 9 cm (3½ in). Spawning takes place near the bottom and the eggs take from five to six months to develop. Since this species is most unsociable

it is advisable to keep individual pairs in isolation. However, since they are beautiful and brightly coloured, breeders are amply rewarded for their pains.

The **Calabar Lyretail**, *Roloffia liberiense*, formerly *Aphyosemion calabricum* [Pl. 22b], comes from the coast of Calabar. The males are larger than the females, being about 5 cm (2 in) long. These fishes prefer to spawn near the bottom; the fry emerge

33 'Moon Platy' (*Xiphophorus maculatus*)

34 'Comet Platy' (*Xiphophorus maculatus*)

as soon as twelve to fourteen days after spawning. This is a very popular species because of its bright colouring. If they are startled, and indeed sometimes for no apparent reason at all, they will leap right out of the tank, through even a very small hole: they must therefore be kept under a firmly fixed glass cover.

Aplocheilichthys is another well represented genus from the waters of West and central Africa. The **Lamp-eyed Panchax,** *Aplocheilichthys macroph-*

thalmus [429], is only 3.5 cm (1½ in) in length. This graceful fish generally hovers near the oxygen supply of an aquarium tank and sometimes swims in and out of the rising bubbles. The process of spawning continues for several days. If several pairs are spawning in the same tank, it is usually best to remove the substratum together with the spawn to another tank after a certain time. The fry are tiny and emerge after ten to fourteen days. These fishes are happiest kept together in a shoal.

430

431

The genus *Epiplatys* lives principally in the waters of tropical West Africa. *Epiplatys annulatus* [430, Pl. 28] from Guinea is a very gay, unusually coloured species with bright light and dark stripes across its body. It is only 3–4 cm (1–1½ in) long. The tail fin of the male iridesces with all the colours of the rainbow. The act of spawning consists of an ordered ceremony in which the colours of the body and the outstretched fins are displayed in their full splendour. The sticky eggs have tiny adhesive threads and are attached to the leaves and roots of aquatic plants. The fry emerge after some six to seven days.

Epiplatys dageti [431], comes from Sierra Leone and Liberia. It is 5.5 cm (2 in) long. The basic colouring consists of olive to grey-green tones; the sides of the body are decorated with between

five and seven black cross-stripes. The male is distinguished by the extended border of his tail fin and a red stripe across the middle of the lower jaw. The spawning period lasts for several weeks. It is advisable to add a little cooking salt to the water and, in order to prevent cannibalism, to remove the plants to which the eggs have been attached into a specially prepared breeding tank. The fry emerge after eight to ten days at a temperature of 25°C. *Epiplatys dageti* is suitable for mixed aquaria, for it is a sociable little fish.

Epiplatys chaperi sheljuzhkoi [433] is about 6 cm (2½ in) long and comes from the neighbourhood of Abidjan in West Africa. This is a robust fish but, although it is comparatively easy to keep and breed, it is not very popular among aquarists and is therefore little known.

434

The **Banded Epiplatys,** *Epiplatys fasciolatus*, has a delicate, blue-violet colour over the whole body [432, Pl. 27]. It is a native of Sierra Leone, Liberia, and Nigeria and first came to the notice of aquarists in 1911. It is easy to keep and the young fishes are able to reproduce when they are 4 cm (1½ in) long. As with most species of the genus *Epiplatys* they do not need particularly soft water. The addition of two teaspoons of sea salt per ten litres of water is recommended for successful breeding. The young hatch after ten to fourteen days.

The next genus, *Nothobranchius*, consists of about twelve short-lived, brightly coloured species from the waters of tropical Africa. Not much is known about their biology in the natural state.

One species from East Africa, *Nothobranchius guentheri* [434], which grows to a length of 7 cm (2½ in), needs soft water if it is to be kept and bred successfully. The young emerge after about three to six weeks and grow astonishingly quickly. At three to four weeks the young fishes already are

435

436

sexually mature. They are unsociable fishes and must be kept in isolated pairs. *Nothobranchius melanospilus* [435, Pl. 29], is very similar although rather more slender than the previous species. The female has dark, irregularly distributed flecks across the whole of her body thus easily distinguishing her from the male. Breeding and rearing are much the same as has already been described for *Nothobranchius guentheri*. *Nothobranchius orthonotus* [436], lives along the east coast of Africa in inlets of the sea, especially in mangrove swamps.

It is a particularly robust species when adult and grows to a length of 7 cm (2½ in). It has been bred successfully in captivity.

One of the most gaily coloured members of the genus is undoubtedly **Rachov's Nothobranchius,** *Nothobranchius taeniopygus* (formerly *Nothobranchius rachovi*) [Pl. 30], from Mozambique. It is 5 cm (2 in) in length. The female, like all species in this genus, is smaller than the male but is more strikingly coloured.

437

438

439

Members of the genus *Pachypanchax* live for several years but are not very popular among aquarists. The fresh and brackish waters of Madagascar are the home of *Pachypanchax homalonotus* [437], which grows to a length of 9.5 cm (3½ in). In spite of its size it is a peace-loving fish and easy to keep. It spawns frequently even in a mixed aquarium provided that there is a sufficient growth of water plants. It is less fussy about the composition of the water than the species of the genus *Nothobranchius*. Its eggs are large and sticky and the fry emerge after twelve to sixteen days. Provided there is sufficient food in a largish tank the adult fishes pay no attention to the fry.

A related species, **Playfair's Panchax,** *Pachy-* *panchax playfairi* [438], lives in East Africa, Madagascar, and on the Seychelles. It grows to a length of 10 cm (4 in) and in contrast to the last mentioned species is very aggressive. Playfair's Panchax is relatively unconcerned about the substratum over which spawning takes place. Picture 439 shows a pair spawning above a gravel bottom; a little later, they bring their eggs into a thicket of water plants [440].

Several genera of Cyprinodonts with a variety of forms inhabit the waters of North, Central, and South America. A species which is often kept in aquaria is the **Cuban Killie,** *Cubanichthys cubensis* [441], which comes from western Cuba. Its length

441

442

is at most 8 cm (3 in) and the male is always larger than the female. Its body is covered with iridescent green spots arranged in rows. The tiny eggs hang like little bunches of grapes from threads in the vicinity of the female's anal fin before they are attached to water plants. The fry emerge after ten to twelve days. This is a very difficult species to keep and breed, and the number of young from each spawning is small.

The **American Flagfish,** *Jordanella floridae* [442] – about 6 cm (2½ in) long – lives in the swamps and lakes of Florida. It has been kept in the aquaria of Europe since 1914. A single pair is content with a comparatively small tank containing only 6–8 litres, but the American Flagfish does require a thick growth of water plants, a dark bottom, and access to the morning sunlight. The fishes feed partly on algae. The male protects the eggs in much the same way as do the Cichlids. The disadvantage of breeding this fish is that even after several generations it does not lose its shyness.

The distribution of the genus *Cynolebias* is confined to the central and southern parts of South America: it is an inhabitant of small pools and puddles. The eggs survive the dry season encased in damp mud. In the aquarium members of this species lay their eggs on a peat bottom. The water in which they are kept needs to be poured out through a very fine strainer after every fifteen to twenty days, while the peat floor in which the eggs are lying should be taken out, gently squeezed to remove some of the water and laid on a flat glass plate. The peat should not be allowed to dry out too quickly and should therefore be sprinkled from time to time with water. After another three weeks it should be put back into water and shortly afterwards the young fish will emerge. They are fed on live plankton.

The **Argentine Pearlfish,** *Cynolebias bellotti* [443], comes from the basin of the river Plate. The male grows to a length of 7 cm (3 in) while the female is smaller.

443

444

The **Black-finned Pearlfish,** *Cynolebias nigripinnis* [444], comes from the Paraná river, above Rosario. This is an attractive, peaceable fish which grows to a length of only 4.5 cm (2 in). Before spawning the male swims rapidly about at various levels of the water, but chiefly close to the bottom, taking up a threatening posture with fins outstretched before the female [445]. If she is ready and willing to mate the female follows the male down to the bottom where he buries his head in the peat [446].

445

446

The female then follows him and both of them disappear briefly to lay their eggs in the peat. The male reappears first followed shortly by the female. *Cynolebias nigripinnis* requires soft water and live plankton when kept in the aquarium.

Cynolebias whitei [447] comes from Brazil. The male is up to 8 cm (3 in) long. This species is dark brown in colouring with a lighter under belly and is covered with rows of light blue spots, which are largest on the head. The dorsal fin is extended and

447

448

449

450

451

is touched with pink. The female has a black mark on her sides. Breeding proceeds in the same manner as described for Cynolebias nigripinnis.

The related genus Pterolebias lives in northern South America. Pterolebias peruensis, which grows to a length of 9 cm (3½ in), comes from the upper Amazon in Peru. Its basic colouring is greyish-brown with dark, iridescent-green cross-stripes, which continue up the dorsal and anal fins. The belly and the gills are golden yellow. The male [448] has elongated fins, while those of the female [449] are shorter and her tail fin is rounded in shape. They lay their eggs in the bed of the aquarium and the development period lasts for three months.

The seasonal rivers north-west of Rio de Janeiro are inhabited by Cynopoecilus ladigesi [450] which is often found in nearly dry pools. It grows to a length of 3.5 cm (1½ in). This species is best kept alone in small tanks. Spawning is accomplished in much the same way as in members of the genus Aphyosemion. Adult specimens like shady recesses and during the day will always seek out the darkest spot in the aquarium.

The genus Rivulus also contains a number of species which are suitable for breeding in captivity. The **Green, Brown,** or **Cuban Rivulus,** Rivulus cylindraceus, which is 5.5 cm (2 in) in length, occurs in Cuba and Florida. Picture 451 shows spawning taking place on a stony bottom.

If this species is to be kept in an aquarium the tank must be properly covered, for the fish will readily leap out. Members of the genus *Rivulus* can be kept in company only with larger fishes, for they are remarkably aggressive.

Hart's Rivulus, *Rivulus harti* [453], lives in the waters of eastern Colombia, Venezuela, and the adjacent islands. It is up to 10 cm (4 in) in length, but in spite of its size it gets on well with smaller fishes. At the root of her tail the female has a dark spot with a light border which is not present in the male. Hart's Rivulus is of considerable local economic importance, for it is frequently preserved in oil or pickled.

Rivulus holmiae, a rarer species which comes from Guiana, grows to a length of 8–10 cm (3–4 in). Picture 454 shows a male. The adults of this species require plenty of space in the aquarium and a rich

growth of water plants. By day they can be found at every level in the water from the bottom up to the surface. They particularly like to sun themselves above a broad leaf.

They usually lay their eggs in a thicket of plants such as the aquatic moss *Fontinalis* [455], but they sometimes spawn on the broad leaves of various species of Cape Pondweed, *Aponogeton* [456]. *Rivulus holmiae* will survive brief exposure to quite low water temperatures, but it is best suited by a temperature of 22–25°C. The fry emerge from the eggs after twelve to fourteen days and feed straight away on *Cyclops* nauplii which they capture with a characteristic darting movement. The young fishes grow quickly; in the second month they are already 4 cm (1½ in) long and after three months sexual differences are apparent.

35   *Bedotia geayi*

36 Bluegill (*Lepomis macrochirus*)

Rivulus marmoratus [457] lives in the fresh waters of Cuba, and the islands of Curacao, Benatre, and Los Roques. According to Hoedeman the typical and original species is a native of Cuba, while specimens found elsewhere in the Antilles form a subspecies Rivulus marmoratus bonairensis. They possess a larger number of fin rays in the dorsal, anal, and pectoral fins.

458

459

The **Santos Rivulus,** *Rivulus santensis* [458] is about 7 cm (3 in) long and occurs in the area between Rio de Janeiro and Santos in Brazil. The male is bright green to yellowish in colouring; the female is brown with blue spots. This fish was first brought to Europe in 1903 but it is not particularly popular although quite simple to keep in aquaria.

The superfamily of Live-bearing Tooth-carps, **Poecilioidae,** contains small fishes from Central America, the islands of the West Indies, the southern states of the USA, and South America down to northern Argentina. Their natural habitat differs widely. The sexual dimorphism of the Poecilioidae is characteristic: the anal fin of the male has been wholly or partly transformed into a genital organ known as the gonopodium. The largest species are no bigger than 20 cm (8 in)

and the males are smaller than the females. They give birth to live young several times a year.

The eastern part of Central America is inhabited by the largest of the Live-bearing Tooth-carps, the **Pike Top Minnow,** *Belonesox belizanus* [459]. The female is up to 20 cm (8 in) long but the male measures no more than 10 cm (4 in). This species is a predator and is unsuitable for mixed aquaria. It lives principally near the surface of the water and requires a large tank with plentiful plant growth. Before mating the male usually takes up a threatening posture [460] in which its gonopodium is stretched out forwards. They are not easy to feed. The adults like to feed on large fragments of fish, dragonfly larvae, tadpoles, and worms. When they reach a length of 12–18 cm (4½–7 in) they are able to consume adult female Platies and Guppies.

460

461

For breeding they require a water temperature of 25–30°C. The differences in coloration are extremely interesting. Picture 461 shows a female and picture 464 a male in their night colouring. Both have an extremely flexible upper jaw [462, 463] enabling them to swallow very large chunks of food. If they are well fed a single spawning produces up to 100 young. The fry are 2.5–3 cm

462

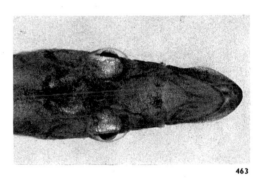

463

464

465

466

(1 in) long and feed straight away on water fleas and white worms. It is not unknown for the female to hunt her new-born young relentlessly.

The **Mosquito Fish, Spotted Gambusia,** or **Texas Gambusia,** *Gambusia affinis*, is among the most well-known of Live-bearing Tooth-carps. This fish plays an important role in the battle against malaria-carrying mosquitos. For this reason it was imported from the southern states of the USA into tropical and subtropical countries throughout the world: it is found in Spain, southern France, Italy, the Balkan Peninsula, southern Rumania, the Ukraine, the Caucasus, and central Asia. It consumes vast quantities of mosquito larvae. The female grows to a length of 6 cm (2½ in) while the male is only 3 cm (1¼ in) long. At the age of one year the fish is able to reproduce. A subspecies, *Gambusia affinis holbrooki* [465], is frequently bred by aquarists. It requires tanks with a plentiful growth of plants, for the female often chases and swallows her own young.

Girardinus metallicus [466] comes from the fresh waters of Cuba. The male – a mere 5 cm (2 in) long – is again considerably smaller than the female. This species is not very brightly coloured and is therefore seldom kept by aquarists. The gonopodium of the male has two horn-like, curved appendages at the end. In the aquarium *Girardinus metallicus* is a peaceable, hardy and long-lived fish. In addition to its diet of animal food it requires a supplementary vegetable diet in the form of algae, lettuce leaves and soaked porridge oats. A single mating produces at most sixty young; these must be protected from the predations of the female. The most suitable aquarium for this fish is a specially constructed breeding tank in which the young fry can escape into a separate chamber through a narrow passage where the female cannot follow.

The **Dwarf Top Minnow** or **Mosquito Fish,** *Heterandria formosa* [467], is one of the smallest fishes – and also one of the smallest vertebrates – in the world. The male is only 2 cm (1 in) long and the female measures about 3.5 cm (1½ in). It lives in waters between North Carolina and Florida, and is a popular species with an inconspicuous brown colouring. It was first introduced into Europe in 1912. It is remarkable for its undemanding qualities and will survive temperatures as low as 15°C. The female is exceptional among Live-bearing Tooth-carps in that she does not hunt her young. The act of giving birth extends over several days, usually six to ten, and on each day only two or three young fishes are born. When food is plentiful the period between fertilization and birth is not longer than four to five weeks. The Dwarf Top Minnow does not require a large aquarium and is not fussy in its diet. Besides animal

468

and vegetable food it will also take dried and artificial food stuff.

One of the most popular Live-bearing Tooth-carps is the **Guppy**, *Poecilia reticulata* (formerly *Lebistes reticulatus*). The Guppy comes from Venezuela, Barbados, Trinidad, north Brazil, and Guiana. The female grows to a length of 6 cm (2½ in) and the male 3 cm (1 in). The Guppy was first imported in 1908 and it is a worthwhile object for breeders in view of the great variations in colouring and form which can be achieved, particularly in the male. Colour plate 31 shows the rainbow colouring of a male. Aquarists have succeeded in achieving a breed which forms the basis of standards for international exhibition. Among the most variable features is the form of the dorsal and tail fins. Picture 468 shows one of the eleven basic forms: the **Veil-tail Guppy**. The gestation period depends on the water temperature and varies between twenty-two and twenty-five days. After this there is a period of rest lasting for seven to nine days followed by the development of a new brood. Pregnant females may be recognized by the black, pregnancy spot in front of the anal fin. A single act of fertilization suffices for between two and three litters. The males are pronouncedly polygamous and are very active partners. Birth itself [469, 470] lasts for up to two hours and is dependent on the temperature of the water, on its chemical composition, and occasionally also on the surrounding, particularly on other fishes. The maternal instinct to protect the young can delay birth by several hours.

The **Black-bellied** or **Blue Limia**, *Poecilia* or *Limia melanogaster* [471], which is about the same size as the Guppy comes from Jamaica. The name *melanogaster* (black belly) refers to the unusually large pregnancy spot which does not entirely disappear after the birth of the young. The Blue Limia prefers sunshine and warmth. Up to eighty young are born during one breeding period.

469
470

471

472

473

474

475

476

The **Hump-back Limia** or **Black-barred Limia,** *Poecilia* or *Limia nigrofasciata* [472], lives in Haiti. The male grows to a length of 4.5 cm (2 in) and the female to 6 cm (2½ in). This fish is especially sensitive to changes in the water. Older specimens usually die if they are subjected to sudden changes in water composition. If they are transferred from one aquarium to another it is recommended that first of all water from the new tank be added to the old one little by little, over a period of several days in order that the fish may accustom themselves better to the new water composition. The Hump-back Limia likes a peaceable life and warm surroundings (22–25°C). It feeds on animal matter but also on algae. The females give birth quite readily but they bear only a few young – at most thirty individuals – at a time. The fry are 10–12 mm (½ in) long. The adult males have a characteristic swelling or hump on the back and a raised orange-coloured rim to the root of the tail fin. The two species of Limias are frequently crossed. The offspring of

a cross between *Poecilia melanogaster* and *Poecilia nigrofasciata* is shown in picture 473.

The **Mollies,** which were formerly considered as a separate genus *Mollienesia* have more recently been placed in the genus *Poecilia.* They have a very wide geographical distribution in the southern States of the USA, Central America, the Caribbean, and northern South America.

The **Sailfin Molly,** *Poecilia velifera* (formerly *Mollienesia velifera*), lives in the coastal regions of Yucatan. In the aquarium it grows to a length of 12 cm (4½ in) and in nature up to 15 cm (6 in). The males [474] have a greatly enlarged dorsal fin. In this species, as also in *Poecilia latipinna* and *Poecilia sphenops*, a large number of colour variations and crosses has been bred. One of the most well-known mutations of *Poecilia latipinna* is known as the 'Black Molly'; picture 475 shows a male. Recently other forms have been bred such as the 'Lyre-tailed Molly' [476], which sometimes occurs as a veiled form, the 'Veiled Molly'.

477

Hybrids of a cross between *Poecilia velifera* and the 'Lyretailed Molly' are shown in picture 477; there are two males and one female. The veiled and other artificially bred forms are generally very demanding and difficult to keep and breed.

The **Caudo, One-spot Livebearer,** or **Dusky Millions Fish,** *Phalloceros caudomaculatus,* lives in waters between Rio de Janeiro, Uruguay, and Paraguay. The females grow to a length of some 6 cm (2½ in), the males 2.5 cm (1 in). These are peaceable and quiet little fishes which enjoy great popularity among aquarists. They will survive very low temperatures, down to 12°C, so that they can be kept in an unheated domestic aquarium. A number of varieties of this species are known,

the most familiar being the '**Piebald Caudo**', *Phalloceros caudomaculatus reticulatus* [478], which is dark spotted and is most numerous in the neighbourhood of Rio de Janeiro. It is warmth-loving and will not survive below 20°C.

The **Black-barred Livebearer,** *Quintana atrizona* [479], lives in Cuba in the neighbourhood of Havana. This species requires warm water at a temperature of about 23–28°C. The female grows to a length of 4 cm (1½ in), the male to about 2.5 cm (1 in). The Black-barred Livebearer feeds on animal remains but also likes algae. It is a peace-loving fish and the adults rarely hunt their young and then only if there is a shortage of food. No more than forty young are born at any one time.

480

481

One of the most beautiful and variable of fishes is the **Swordtail**, *Xiphophorus helleri*, which lives in Guatemala and southern Mexico in rivers flowing to the east. The female grows to a length of about 12 cm (4½ in) and the male is normally smaller. The original wild form is green in colouring and the closest artificially bred form is the green '**Simpson Swordtail**' [480], distinguished by its veil-shaped dorsal fin. Very often a number of red variations are bred, for example the so-called '**Wagtailed Swordtail**' or '**Black-finned Swordtail**' [481]. The two variations just described were crossed

482

483

to produce the '**Red Wagtail Swordtail**': picture 482 shows a male, picture 483 a female. The '**Tuxedo Swordtail**' [484], which has black sides to its body with a green iridescence, was crossed with the '**Simpson**' to produce the '**Tuxedo-Simpson Swordtail**' [485]. In addition to the colour variations mentioned many more are known which are usually named after their area of distribution or

484

487

after the breeder. Picture 486 shows the so-called **Berlin Cross.** In recent years quite a sensation was created when a **'Double Swordtail'** or **'Lyretail Xiphophorus'** was achieved. The male is illustrated in picture 487, the female in picture 488. The Swordtails are peaceable fishes in spite of their size. They are hardy and omnivorous, and give birth to as many as 200 young at a time.

488

37 Black Bass *(Micropterus salmoides)*

Plectorhinchus albovittatus

Similar variations are found in another species, the **Platy**, *Xiphophorus maculatus*, which has the same geographical area of distribution as the Swordtail. The original form is olive-brown in colouring. However, even in nature black specimens are frequently found, and artificial breeding has produced a wide variety of colour variations, of which the **Red** or **Gold Platy** is the most popular. It has orange to blood-red colouring. A very high value is placed on specimens with ivory-coloured tips to the fins [Pl. 32b]. A closely related form is the red '**Wagtail Platy**' which has black fins [489]. The '**Tuxedo Platy**' is either yellow [490] or red [491].

The male of the '**Calico Platy**' [492], is flecked with black. The '**Moon Platy**' [Pl. 33] and the '**Comet Platy**' [Pl. 34] are streaked with shades of yellow and orange. Unfortunately the illustrations do not capture the full beauty of this splendid little fish; it must be seen to be properly appreciated. The Platy is about 6 cm (2½ in) long and has fewer offspring in a single brood than the Swordtail – a maximum of 100 individuals.

A third species, not less rich in variety, is the **Variegated Platy**, *Xiphophorus variatus* [493], from southern Mexico. The female grows to

491

a length of 7 cm (2½ in) and the males are smaller. Here too there is a large number of distinct races with many colour variations achieved by artificial breeding. Picture 494 shows a flecked male. The male of the veiled form [495] is orange in colouring and possesses a large, veil-like dorsal fin, which when erected often extends beyond the tail fin. The orange-coloured '**Meri-gold Platy**' [496] is almost unimaginably beautiful. The male [Pl. 32a] has a lemon-yellow back and dorsal fins, while the root of the tail fin is deep red. In the course of artificial breeding some specimens have arisen –

492

493

particularly females – which have narrow, black, vertical stripes on their flanks [497].

The next group of families, which belong to the order **Beryciformes,** resemble the Perches. Their many-rayed pelvic fins are just beneath or slightly behind the pectoral fins. The pelvic fins are usually equipped with a spine and between three and thirteen branched fin rays. The number of main rays in the tail fin is nineteen of which seventeen are branched. There is a number of strong spines before both dorsal and anal fins. The Soldierfishes

494

495

496

or Squirrelfishes **Holocentridae** live in the Atlantic, the Pacific, and Indian oceans. The best known genus is *Holocentrus*, represented by numerous tropical species.

Holocentrus ruber [498] is frequently kept in aquaria. Its geographical distribution is extremely wide. It is most commonly caught in the neighbourhood of New Guinea, Japan, Sumatra, and the Philippines.

499

The distribution of *Holocentrus diadema* [499] extends from the Red Sea to Tahiti and the Hawaiian Islands. This species has striking red colouring and white stripes on its flanks. The spiny anterior part of the dorsal fin is black with red spots. In nature this fish has a maximum length of 19 cm (7½ in).

The **Black-tipped Soldierfish**, *Myripristis murdjan* [500] has a similar range to *Holocentrus diadema*. In contrast to the members of the genus *Holocentrus* it has a broad head, a comparatively short body, and enormous eyes. It is red with large scales which are white in the middle, and it grows to

a length of about 35 cm (14 in). In Hawaii Black-tipped Soldierfishes are caught in ground nets. One fish is first tied to the net; other Soldierfishes are then attracted by its unusual behaviour. When a sufficient number has collected the net is raised with the captive shoal.

The **Mugiliformes** (Grey Mullets) have their pelvic fins placed well back on the belly. They have a spiny dorsal fin separated from the branched, rayed fin. The scales are present on the head. These are principally pelagic fishes of the open sea or coastal waters of the tropics and subtropics, but some species are found in temperate waters.

500

502

503

504

More than twenty species belonging to the Barracuda family **(Sphyraenidae)** have been described. The **Great Barracuda**, *Sphyraena barracuda* [501], is generally caught in the Caribbean and off northern Brazil. It grows to a length of 2.5 m (8 ft). The **European Barracuda**, *Sphyraena sphyraena*, lives in the Black Sea and the Mediterranean; *Sphyraena jello*, measuring 3 m (10 ft) and weighing 25 kg (55 lb), comes from the coastal waters of Africa and Asia. All species of Barracudas are much feared predators. Large specimens have been known to attack swimmers and cause fatal injuries.

The family **Mugilidae** (Grey Mullets) contains more than 100 species which are present in all but the coldest seas of the world. They often swim up into the brackish waters of river estuaries. They have a muscular gizzard in which they masticate their food — mainly algae and detritus browsed and grubbed from the bottom. Their teeth are minute and their intestine long, both features of herbivorous fishes.

The **Striped Grey Mullet**, *Mugil cephalus*, is present in all warm seas. It is up to 1 m (3 ft) in length and 8 kg (18 lb) in weight, and feeds principally on algae and diatoms. The 40 cm (16 in) long *Mugil saliens* [502] lives in the Black Sea and the

Adriatic. The **Thick-lipped Grey Mullet**, *Crenimugil labrosus* [503], is widely distributed in European seas and is distinguished by a broad upper lip. It grows to a length of 20 cm (8 in). Grey Mullet eggs are pelagic and in southern Europe are salted and sold as a substitute for caviar. The flesh is tasty and although at times said to be poisonous this is probably only true of particular localities in relation to the feeding habits of Mullets. In some places even the contents of the Grey Mullet's stomach are regarded as a delicacy. Grey Mullets prefer muddy shallow water. They are clever, lively fishes and are difficult to catch on the line.

The **Atherinidae** (Silversides or Sandsmelts) contain several genera of small fishes of up to 35 cm (14 in) in length. Some species have ctenoid and others cycloid scales. They live principally in tropical seas, in brackish water, and estuarine fresh water, but others are known in temperate waters including British seas. Some fresh-water species are kept by aquarists but there is nothing remarkable about them.

The 4.5 cm (2 in) long *Pseudomugil signifer* [504] lives in Australia in the waters of northern and eastern Queensland. It is a lively fish which prefers to swim about in shoals.

505

506

The **Dwarf** or **Black-lined Rainbowfish,** *Mel-anotaenia maccullochi* [505] comes from the neighbourhood of Cairns in northern Australia. It grows to a length of 7 cm (3 in). In the aquarium it is a peace-loving and undemanding member of the community which will feed equally happily on living or dried food. It should be kept in tanks which have plenty of light and are accessible at least to the morning sun. Its eggs are equipped with short threads by which they are attached to water plants. The young emerge at a water temperature of 25°C after seven to ten days. They are dark in colour and at first are attached to the walls of the aquarium and the leaves of the plants. Shortly afterwards they begin to swim about, remaining close to the surface of the water. In the first few days they should be fed on living plankton; later they will also take dried food. A single spawning will produce between 150 and 200 young. There are no particular difficulties encountered in breeding them.

The waters of Australia southwards as far as Sydney contain a relative of the Dwarf Rainbowfish, the **Australian Red-tailed Rainbowfish,** *Melanotae-nia nigrans* [506]. It grows to a length of 10 cm (4 in) and will survive well at a room temperature of 18–20°C. A little salt should be put in the water, whereupon the fish readily brightens up.

The waters of Celebes and the hinterland of Makasar are inhabited by the **Celebes Sailfish** or **Celebes Rainbowfish,** *Telmatherina ladigesi* [507], which is 7 cm (3 in) long. Because it is very shy the aquarium should be large and well-planted with water flora. It requires living foodstuff, frequent changes of at least part of the water, and efficient water filtration. The spawn is laid on fine-leafed water plants. The eggs are yellow and the fry emerge after eight to ten days if they escape the predations of their parents. After about seven months the young fishes are mature.

Bedotia geayi [508], which reaches a length of 7–8 cm (2½–3 in), comes from Madagascar. For breeding purposes it requires alkaline, hard water. In spite of its size it is peaceful and lively. The male [Pl. 35] is differentiated from the female principally by the red ends of his tail fin and richer colouring.

508

509

Both forks of the tail fin of the female are transparent or whitish. The male initiates spawning by driving the female through the aquarium. He often remains in a position above her [509]. *Bedotia geayi* prepares to spawn in much the same way as the Harlequin Fish. Spawning usually lasts for several days during which a few eggs are laid each day. Both the eggs and the fry are protected by the parents. The young fishes feed from the outset on newly emerged brine shrimps *(Artemia)*.

The order **Ophicephaliformes** (Snakeheads) contains fishes which are distinguished by a cylindrical body. The swimbladder is closed and the pelvic fins are located beneath and immediately behind the pectoral fins. The head is covered with scales. They possess an auxiliary respiratory organ in the gill chamber which is adapted for breathing oxygen from the air. Their habitat lies in warm, muddy waters; they require a high water temperature. About forty species are known. The genus *Ophicephalus* is represented by several species in Asia and central Africa. *Ophicephalus striatus* is found in India and grows to a length of 1 m (3 ft). It is often caught for its tasty flesh which is highly valued. *Ophicephalus argus warpachowski* [510] occurs in

the region of the Amur river and grows to a length of 85 cm (34 in) with a weight of 7 kg (15 lb). It lays its eggs — as many as 15,000 at one sitting — in nests built from plant matter. The male watches over the nest. Attempts have been made to introduce these fishes into the European part of the Soviet Union since it survives in places where neither Tench nor Carp can withstand the lack of oxygen.

The most numerous order of the living Bony Fishes is the **Perciformes**. Its members generally have two dorsal fins of which the first has only hard, spiny fin rays. The pelvic fins are found underneath the pectoral fins. The scales are generally ctenoid. This order embraces some twenty suborders whose members appear as early as the Upper Cretaceous. The Perciformes are principally sea fishes, some of which have great economic importance.

The suborder **Percoidei** contains several families which live in both fresh and salt water. The family **Centropomidae**, Glassfishes, contains the **Indian Glassfish**, *Chanda ranga* [511], which is a popular breeding species among aquarists. These fishes live in the waters of India, Burma and Thailand.

331

511

512

513

They grow to a length of 7 cm (3 in) and are equally happy in fresh or slightly salt water. The Indian Glassfish spawns in thickets of water plants and the fry emerge after only twenty-four hours at a temperature of 28°C. For a further three to four days the young hang on the walls of the aquarium or on the plants. At first they swim in a vertical position with the head upwards and in this way hunt their food. They are extremely fussy and are not satisfied with the almost unmoving, easily caught rotifers. If they do not find *Cyclops* nauplii they promptly die. However, if their food is acceptable, within two or three days they change posi-

tion and swim horizontally. At this point they will feed on plankton of all kinds.

Chanda wolffi [512], which comes from Thailand, Sumatra, and Borneo is a relative of the Indian Glassfish. It grows to a length of 20 cm (8 in) in nature, although in the aquarium it rarely reaches more than 6–7 cm (2½–3 in). It has not yet been bred successfully in captivity and little is known about its sexual dimorphism.

Members of the family **Serranidae** are familiar and widely distributed sea fishes, representatives

514

515

of which are found as early as the Eocene. They are encountered principally in tropical and subtropical seas although some of them are found in temperate waters and others live in fresh water. There is a number of genera in this family. *Serranus* contains more than 200 species some of which swim quite a long way up rivers. Really natural photographs of these fishes in their own habitat can only be achieved by a skin diver with an underwater camera [513], and only then if he is able to slip quietly and without disturbance into their under-sea world. In fact the fishes accustom themselves quickly to the presence of a diver and behave quite normally.

Serranus scriba, the **Banded Sea-perch**, is an inhabitant of the Adriatic and Mediterranean and prefers to spend much of its time in rocky caves [514]; picture 515 shows it emerging to hunt. It grows to a length of 28 cm (11 in). Its basic colouring is orange to red with bluish vertical stripes. It is a little smaller than the **Gaper** or **Comber**, *Serranus cabrilla* [516], which is up to 34 cm (13 in) long. All species of *Serranus* have very tasty flesh even if they are only small. Both species mentioned are hermaphrodites. Their genital organs develop simultaneuosly and they can fertilize themselves.

39   *Chaetodon chrysurus*

40 Ringed Emperor Angelfish *(Pomacanthodes annularis)*

The **Belted Sand-fish,** *Serranellus subligarius* [517], lives at moderate depths off the coasts of the southern states of the USA. It has been caught from time to time in the neighourhood of Beaufort, Charleston and Pensacola. It is sometimes kept in aquaria by reason of its attractive colouring.

517

The **Groupers,** genus *Epinephelus,* consist of a large number of species which grow to quite a large size. Native populations in many countries find them a valuable foodstuff. The Groupers are the largest and economically the most important fishes of the family Serranidae and they also have the widest geographical area of distribution. Their principal distinguishing features are rounded pectoral fins and the comparatively small number of pyloric appendages (ten to twenty) in the intestines. The number of fin rays is in the region of fifteen to twenty. Most species are very brightly coloured and about 400 of them are distributed throughout the seas of the tropics and subtropics, with a very few in temperate seas.

The **Purple Rock Cod,** *Epinephelus flavocaeruleus* [518], has a bluish body which is irregularly covered with large and small spots. The fins and lips are light yellow. The purple colouring stretches about half way up the dorsal and anal fins. This fish is 40 cm (16 in) long and ranges from the Red Sea throughout the seas of southern and eastern Asia as far as China and the Pacific.

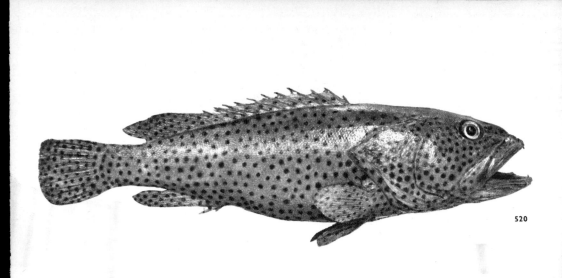

520

The **Nassau Grouper,** *Epinephelus striatus* [519], has short abdominal fins. Its basic colouring is a light olive-grey with dark, irregular, wavy cross-stripes. It is found principally around the West Indies and along the coast of Brazil. The Nassau Grouper is prized for its excellent taste. It grows to a length of 1 m (3 ft).

Individual species of the genus *Epinephelus* are sometimes brought to Europe and kept in large public aquaria. The most common are *Epinephelus salonotus* [520] and the **Speckled Hind,** *Epine-*

phelus drummondhayi [521]. The latter weighs up to 14 kg (3 lb) and is caught from the Gulf of Mexico to north of the Bermudas. Its bright colouring does not fade in captivity, making it a particularly good fish for aquarists.

The **Merou,** *Epinephelus guaza* (formerly *Epinephelus gigas*) [522], is extremely common in the Mediterranean and Adriatic seas and can grow to a very large size. It is usually solitary, living among rocks and in caves. The larger specimens establish a territory for themselves.

521

522

523

524

A striking fish which is sometimes kept in sea-water aquaria is the **'Panther'** or **'Grace Kelly Fish'**, *Cromileptes altivelis* [523]. It has broad, extended dorsal and anal fins and the whole body is covered with dark spots. The whole appearance of the fish with its flattened back and small down-turned mouth is very unusual. It lives in the Indian Ocean and grows to a length of 50 cm (20 in).

Although the genus *Promicrops* has a more robust body, it was formerly often included in the genus *Epinephelus* from which it differs only in some details of the anatomy of the skull and in its larger dimensions. Some species of *Promicrops* live in the

Pacific and Atlantic oceans although their exact area of distribution has not been definitely determined. The largest is probably the **Australian jewfish,** *Promicrops lanceolatus,* which grows to a length of 3.7 m (12 ft) and weighs 450 kg (990 lb). It lives near the sea bottom throughout the Indo-Pacific region, particularly along the north Australian coast. A young specimen is shown in picture 524.

The **Six-line Grouper,** *Grammistes sexlineatus,* has a highly variable colouring, adult specimens are dark brown to black, with white to creamy-yellow stripes along the sides. The younger fishes have rows of flecks of varying size [525]. A specimen 3 cm (1½ in) in length has three stripes while one of 5 cm (2 in) has four, and at a length of 6 cm (2½ in) there are already six stripes along the fish. By the time the fish reaches a size of 11 cm (4½ in) it has eleven to twelve stripes down each side of its body. The Six-line Grouper lives around coral reefs either alone or in small groups of two to three. It is a comparatively popular fish for seawater aquaria. If it is taken out of the aquarium the other inhabitants quickly die. For a long time this phenomenon caused considerable bewilderment but it is now thought that when it is frightened it exudes a poisonous secretion.

The species *Gramma hemichrysos* [526] is among the most beautifully coloured of fishes. Its body is purple, while the head and fins at the front of the body are dark blue and the tail changes from a deep red to yellow. This fish is 6 cm (2½ in) long and lives in the coral reefs of the Caribbean at a depth of more than 4 m (13 ft). It is frequently kept in aquaria but it is demanding, very sensitive, and a victim of abscesses which start at the root of the tail and quickly spread over the whole body. *Gramma hemichrysos* defends its territory vigorously against other members of the species. It requires crystal clear water and a temperature of 28°C.

The **Centrarchidae** (Sunfishes and Black Basses) are exclusively fresh-water fishes, although a few species will live in brackish water. The spiny front part of the single dorsal fin is shorter than the soft rayed part. There are many genera some of which have considerable economic importance in North America. With a few exceptions they all have a high body and bright colouring. During the spawning season the males hollow out a dish-like spawning bed in the gravel of the bottom and they also watch over the spawn and fry.

The eastern and central states of the USA are inhabited by the **Peacockeyed Bass,** *Centrarchus macropterus* [527], which achieves a length of 16 cm (6 in). In the aquarium it reaches maturity when 8 cm (3 in) long. It was first brought to Europe in 1906. The mating play of these fishes is remarkable:

they strike each other with lightning movements of the anal fin which can become so rapid that one cannot see them with the naked eye.

The **Dwarf** or **Pigmy Sunfish,** *Elassoma evergladei*

[528], is only 3.5 cm (1½ in) long. Some authors put this into an independent family **Elassomidae.** Its area of distribution stretches from North Carolina to Florida. It is easy to keep and breed and one

530

531

spawning will give between thirty and sixty eggs. The fry emerge after two to three days and feed on free-swimming plankton. The adults neither care for nor attack their spawn and fry. The Dwarf Sunfish has been a popular aquarium fish in Europe since 1925: it can survive a fall in water temperature down to 8–12°C.

The **Banded** or **Blue-spotted Sunfish**, *Enneacanthus gloriosus* [529], lives in the waters of the eastern states of the USA from New York to Florida. Older specimens tend to lose their stripes with time. The body is covered with iridescent blotches. It grows to a length of 8 cm (3 in) and is only rarely kept by aquarists.

The genus *Lepomis* was formerly divided into several genera. The **Pumpkinseed Sunfish**, *Lepomis gibbosus* (formerly *Eupomotis gibbosus*) [530], grows to a length of 20 cm (8 in). Its distribution area stretches from Dakota to the Gulf of Mexico. The fish is only of local economic significance. At the end of the last century it was brought to Europe and is kept there both in aquaria and fish ponds: it has taken naturally to various European waters being found sometimes in the Danube and the Elbe. This is of no direct economic importance, although it can reproduce in such large numbers that it has a deleterious effect on the stock of other fishes.

The **Bluegill**, *Lepomis macrochirus* [Pl. 36], lives in still waters east of the Rocky Mountains from south-

ern Canada to the Gulf of Mexico. Its tasty flesh makes it a popular food fish and it is excellent sport.

The **Black-banded Sunfish**, *Mesogonistius chaetodon* [531], lives in standing and slow-moving waters between New Jersey and Maryland. In the aquarium it rarely exceeds half its natural length of 10 cm (4 in). It has been bred in Europe since 1897. The Black-banded Sunfish is very undemanding and can survive drops in the water temperature down to freezing point. However, it requires crystal clear water and live food. The eggs are laid in hollows made in the bottom; the male watches over the spawn. During the spawning the female takes on an intense colouring and her orange pelvic fins are particularly striking.

The **Largemouth** or **Black Bass**, *Micropterus salmoides* [532, Pl. 37], is found throughout the United States from the Rocky Mountains southwards to Mexico and Florida. It has also been put out in other places in America and Europe. It prefers lakes with clear water and overgrown banks. The Black Bass spawns in the spring at a depth of 60–180 cm (2–6 ft) on a sandy bottom where the male builds a shallow, dish-like spawning bed. Until they reach a length of 2.5 cm (1 in) the young shelter in shoals in folds of the skin of the male. One spawning comprises on average of 4,000 young, and in the wild they reach a weight of 4–8 kg (8–16 lb). The Black Bass has been kept in European fish ponds as a sport fish since the end of the last century.

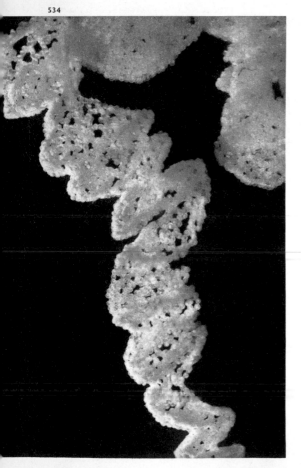

534

Members of the family **Percidae** (Perches) have a dorsal fin divided into two distinct sections. The first part has hard, spiny fin rays, while the fin rays of the second are mostly soft and branched. There are one or two spines in the anal fin. Various species of Perches live in North America, Europe and southern Asia.

The **Common Perch,** *Perca fluviatilis* [533], is a very well known fish of streams, rivers, and ponds, which weighs up to 5 kg (11 b). At the end of the first dorsal fin it possesses a characteristic black fleck. It occurs throughout Europe except in northern Scotland, Norway, and the peninsulas of southern Europe. In Asia it lives in the rivers which flow into the Arctic Ocean as far east as the Kolyma river. The **Yellow Perch,** *Perca flavescens,* which is found in North America, is very closely related and may be no more than a subspecies. The Perch spawns in spring at a temperature of 8–10°C. Its eggs hang in curtain-like rows [534] and are laid on water plants, on submerged twigs and occasionally even on fish traps and nets. Larger specimens spawn up to 20,000 eggs at one time. Picture 535 shows a Perch embryo fifty hours after the fertilization of the egg. The yolk sac with its nourishing yolk and oil droplet is strikingly large. At a water temperature of 15–17°C the embryo is recognizably divided into segments after 110 hours: the tail is already extended and the position of the eyes is visible on the head [536]. After 180 hours the embryo will react to alterations in the intensity of the light or to swift movement against the outside of the egg. Its tail portion is by now equal to half the length of the body [537]. After they

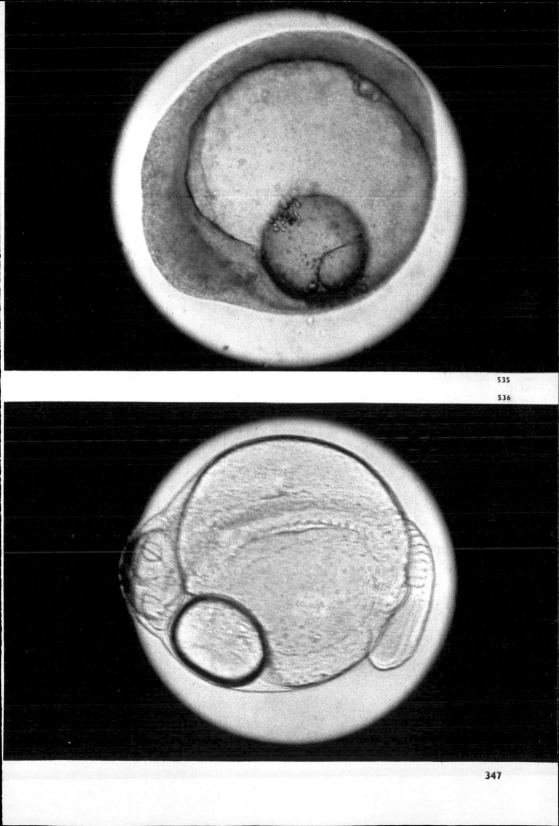

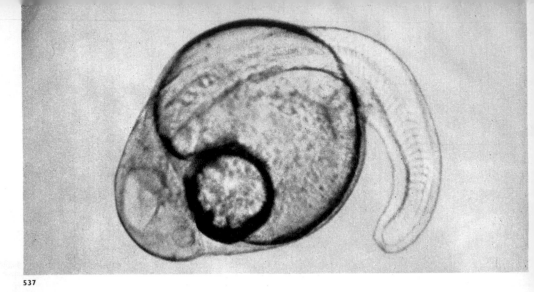

537

emerge the fry swim immediately, and after two or three days they begin to take live food. However, the remains of the yolk persist for more than fourteen days if the fry are well fed. Perches grow most quickly in the first year of their life: in this period they reach a length of 5–10 cm (2–4 in). Individuals from the same brood generally swim about in shoals which are often quite large [538].

The genus *Stizostedion* contains several species which live in North America and in Europe. The European species were formerly included in the genus *Lucioperca*.

The **Pike-Perch** or **Zander**, *Stizostedion lucioperca* [539], grows to a length of 1.3 m (4 ft) and weighs 15 kg (33 lb). Its geographical distribution extends

538

from the Elbe eastwards to the Amu-Darya, southwards to the Maritsa river in Bulgaria, and as far north as the Arctic Circle. It lives in deep rivers with clean water but can also be bred in small fish ponds as long as there is a constant and plentiful supply of flowing water. It prepares nests of reeds and grass roots in which to lay its eggs. The parents are said to care for the spawn and fry. This fish feeds on large insects and small fishes. The Pike-Perch is a popular sport fish on account of its tasty flesh.

The **Ruffe** or **Pope**, *Gymnocephalus cernua* [540], is usually 15 cm (6 in) long but sometimes reaches 25 cm (10 in). It prefers a sandy bottom in lakes and the lower courses of rivers. It is distributed very widely from eastern England to the Kolyma but is not found in Ireland, Scotland, western and northern Norway, or in the peninsulas of southern Europe. It is of no economic significance except as a predator or competitor of other fishes.

The **Zingel**, *Zingel zingel* [541], has a maximum length of 48 cm (19 in) and weighs up to 1 kg (2 lb). It lives in the tributaries of the Danube and the Dniester. It feeds principally on bottom dwelling invertebrates and small fishes. It is not a fast-moving fish and lives at various depths in the water.

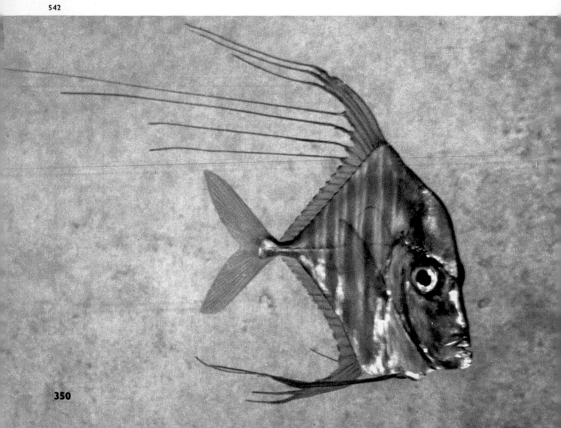

541

Some of the Jacks, Scads and Pilotfishes of the family **Carangidae** resemble the Tunas and Mackerels in body form, but differ from them in many ways. They are known from as early as the Eocene but at the present day are only found in warm seas although a few species occur in temperate oceans. They feed on zooplankton and, as they grow, on small fishes. The **Moonfish,** *Selene vomer* – a very common member of this family – occurs in the tropical Atlantic and Pacific oceans. In young specimens one or two rays of the dorsal fin are extended in a thread-like process. In the **Thread-fish,** *Alectis ciliaris* [542], younger specimens have extremely long, thread-like processes extending from the soft fin rays of the dorsal fin and also on the pelvic and anal fins. The length of these rays often exceeds that of the body. With increasing age they become shorter or disappear entirely. This fish also lives in both the Atlantic and Pacific. The cosmopolitan **Pilotfish,** *Naucrates ductor*, which may grow to a length of 70 cm (28 in) and is distinguished by five to seven lateral, black bars, also belongs to the Carangidae. It often accompanies sharks, turtles and even boats for great distances, presumably deriving protection and concealment by keeping in their shadow.

542

The **Lutjanidae** (Snappers) comprise about twenty genera in more than 250 species, living principally in warm seas. Their bodies are long and covered with cycloid scales (in some instances ctenoid scales occur). The lateral line organ is well developed and the head is broad. They are active predators.

The **Emperor Snapper,** *Lutjanus sebae* [543], is distributed principally in the Indo-Pacific region but is also found in the waters of South Africa. It grows to a length of 100 cm (39 in) and is brightly coloured. The Red Emperor, like its relative *Lutjanus duodecimlineatus* [544], is often kept in public aquaria.

544

351

545

The genus *Aphareus* is widespread throughout the warm seas of the world. The **Job-fish**, *Aphareus furcatus* [545], is found almost everywhere in the equatorial waters of the Pacific Ocean. Its tail fin has a characteristic deep cleft.

The numerous species of the genus *Lutjanus* are characterized by a long head and a body with flattened sides and occur principally in the warm

546

seas around America and Africa. They are predators whose flesh is prized as a delicacy. The **Mutton Snapper**, *Lutjanus analis* [546], is frequently found in the waters of the West Indies, on the coasts of Brazil, and in the Caribbean. It can always be bought in every fish market in Havana. Its flesh is said to have medicinal properties; it is certainly tasty although not very tender. The Muttonfish often reaches a length of 50 cm (20 in).

The chief area of distribution of the genus *Macolor* lies in the tropical waters of the Pacific Ocean. The adult *Macolor niger* is caught at depths of 30–40 cm (100–140 ft) around islands with coral reefs (Bikini Atoll and the Philippines). Its colouring changes as it grows until it is entirely black. At 10 cm (4 in) the fish has black and white markings; not until it reaches a length of 30 cm (12 in) is it mature and entirely black. Eventually it grows to a length of 75 cm (30 in). *Macolor niger* feeds on plankton which it filters from the water through a well-developed net of gill rakers.

The following two genera, *Anisotremus* and *Plectorhinchus*, are put together in a separate family by some authors while others place them in the **Pomadasyidae** or the **Haemulidae** (Grunts).

41   Blue Angelfish (*Pomacanthodes semicirculatus*)

42 *Pomacanthodes chrysurus*

547

548

549

The genus *Anisotremus* lives in the Atlantic and Pacific oceans.

The **Porkfish**, *Anisotremus virginicus* [548], derives its specific name from Virginia although it is not often found so far north, being common between Florida and Brazil. Its basic colouring is an iridescent grey with seven yellow stripes along the sides. The fins too are deep yellow. In young specimens the front region of the body is paler and there is a yellow stripe running from the lower jaw to the leading edge of the dorsal fin which is equipped with stout spines. The pelvic and anal fins are bright golden-yellow in colour, but the remaining fins are paler. At the root of the tail

fin there is a large, black spot and three black stripes pass along both sides of the body. The Porkfish grows to a length of 30 cm (12 in). The young act as 'cleaner-fishes', removing parasites from other species.

The genus *Plectorhinchus* (Sweetlips) contains four species ranging from the Red Sea through the Indian Ocean to the East Indies and the Marshall Islands. One of the most beautiful, although rarely imported, species, is the **Harlequin Sweetlip**, *Plectorhinchus chaetodonoides* [549]. The Harlequin Sweetlip is easy to keep and fits well into an aquarium with various species of Clownfishes, but it requires a diet of live snails *(Mysis)*. In the

aquarium it glides swiftly through the water. The basic colouring is light brown with large, white, black-rimmed marks. In larger specimens, which may be up to 45 cm (18 in) long, the colouring is not so impressive. It lives off the islands of Indonesia, Melanesia and the Philippines. The Sweetlips have stripes along the sides of their body, particularly when young. These are white or yellow, against dark brown or black. The pattern is characteristic for each species although the number, form, and direction of the stripes often varies within the species and depends on the size of the individual. With most aquarium specimens it is not known exactly where they have originated and for this reason it is sometimes difficult or even impossible to be precise about assigning them to a species. This is the case with picture 550 which is probably *Plectorhinchus lineatus*, the **Yellow-banded Sweetlip**, and picture 551, which appears to be *Plectorhinchus sebae*, the **Silver-banded Sweetlip**. The fish illustrated in picture 552 can, on the basis of its outward appearance, only be attributed to *Plectorhinchus* rather than any one species. These three pictures show quite clearly how varied and different from each other young specimens of this genus can be. Among the species which are regularly introduced to Europe from the Indian Ocean is *Plectorhinchus albovittatus* [Pl. 38]. While young it is very brightly coloured and easy to keep. The broad lips and the lateral stripes are quite striking. The lighter stripes are white, golden-yellow, or orange, while the dark ones are black to brown. These stripes disappear as the fish matures and it becomes a uniform grey brown. Black patches, however, remain on the dorsal, tail, and anal fins. The fish grows to a length

of 35 cm (14 in) and in the aquarium feeds principally on molluscs, but it also takes small fishes. It grows remarkably quickly.

The family **Sciaenidae** contains possibly eighty genera and more than 150 species. They live principally in coastal waters of warm seas. Their scales are ctenoid and extend right across the head. There are two dorsal fins of which the second is the longer. Some species are able to emit a noise by using their swim-bladder as a resonance chamber to amplify the sounds produced by the strong muscles attached to it. This ability to make a noise is present particularly in species which live in shoals. These fishes are of great economic significance, for each year some 700,000 tons of them are caught of which 600,000 of them come from the Pacific Ocean alone. The only fresh-water species, the **Fresh-water Drum**, *Aplodinotus grunniens*, lives in the rivers of the east coast of America from Guatemala to Hudson Bay. These fishes are up to 30 kg (66 lb) in weight. Their drumming sound is heard at evening and it is difficult to ascertain the direction from which it comes. In Red Indian mythology the sounds are ascribed to spirits.

The **Atlantic Shade Fish**, *Sciaena aquila*, lives in the Atlantic Ocean and is occasionally taken in British waters. This species grows to a length of 2 m (6 ft) and weighs 200 kg (440 lb).

A whole series of smaller species belonging to the genus *Equetus* are kept in aquaria. The **Jack-Knife Fish**, *Equetus lanceolatus* [553], ranges from the West Indies, north-west to Pensacola and the

553

coasts of Florida. It is about 25 cm (10 in) long and is an attractive little sea fish as is its relative the **Striped Drum**, *Equetus pulcher* [554], which has the same geographical distribution but is at most 20 cm (8 in) long. Both species live in shallow water and are frequently found around coral reefs. The **Corb**, *Corvina nigra* [556], is frequently caught in the Mediterranean and Adriatic. The back of this species is brown, while the sides are golden-yellow to bronze, and the abdomen is silvery-white.

554

The length is up to 52 cm (20 in). The upper jaw is longer than the lower. Corbs are often caught by inshore fishermen in the Mediterranean, and their flesh, although edible, is not highly prized. The family **Sparidae,** Porgies or Sea Breams, consists of species with a high body, flattened at the sides. They possess a single dorsal fin, the front part of which has stout spines, and large teeth of which the back teeth are usually broad and blunt and serve to masticate the prey. More than 250 species are known, placed in a large number of genera. Some members of the genera *Boops*, *Diplodus* and *Pagellus* are known to be normally hermaphrodite. Some species live in shoals.

The **Little-head Porgy,** *Calamus proridens* [555], occurs from north-east Florida southwards to the Gulf of Mexico. It lives in loose shoals in turtle grass and is occasionally found among reefs. It is wary of danger but does not hide away altogether. The **Saupe,** *Sarpa salpa* [557], is up to 10 cm (4 in) long and is coloured grey-blue to olive-green with golden-yellow lateral stripes. The colouring of larger specimens is less striking. The maximum

length and weight are 50 cm (20 in) and 2 kg (4½ lb) respectively. This fish is very common in the Mediterranean and Adriatic where it lives in shoals along the coast and feeds on algae.

Picture 558 shows *Charax puntazzo* and three specimens of *Oblada melanura* from the Adriatic. The first mentioned species has seven to nine vertical stripes on its body. It is 50 cm (20 in) long while *Oblada melanura* is at most 30 cm (12 in).

562

The genus *Diplodus* lives in the Mediterranean basin and on the Atlantic coasts of North America. *Diplodus vulgaris* [559], from southern Europe, has two dark vertical stripes on its body. One is situated behind the head and the other connects the end of the body with the root of the tail. This fish may be up to 40 cm (16 in) long. A related species, *Diplodus sargus* [560], is larger and, indeed, can grow to a length of 50 cm (20 in). It differs from the preceding species in its colouring: the sides of its body are lined with a row of vertical stripes which become less noticeable as the creature grows older. A relative from the coasts of North America is the **Sheepshead**, *Archsargus rhomboidalis* (formerly *Sargus ovis*).

The **Mullidae** (Red Mullets) are distinguished by a low body covered in thin scales. The first dorsal fin is equipped with flexible spines. The **Red Mullet**, *Mulus surmuletus* [561], is a native of both southern and northern coasts of Europe. It is coloured brown and grows to a length of 40 cm (16 in), while the related **Unstriped Red Mullet**, *Mullus barbatus*, lives in the Black Sea and the Mediterranean and is a striking red colour. This fish was highly prized by the Romans. It is said to have been brought to the table alive so that the guests could observe the changes in colouring after its death. Its eggs are pelagic. *Mullus barbatus* has considerable economic significance: each year between 400 and 1,400 tons of them are caught.

563

Related tropical species are popular in aquaria. Like the foregoing species they have two barbels on the lower jaw and are quite brightly coloured. The Goatfishes, *Upeneus* [562] and *Pseudupeneus*, are represented by a large number of species of tropical fishes and are distributed mainly in South Africa, India, the East Indies, the Hawaiian Islands, and around Florida.

The Fingerfishes, **Monodactylidae,** live in the warmer parts of the Indian and Pacific oceans. They have large eyes and a high, compressed body with thin scales. Some of them migrate up rivers. The

564

Common Fingerfish, *Monodactylus argenteus* [563], lives in the Indian Ocean and also on the coasts of eastern Africa and Australia. It is 23 cm (9 in) long and the first dorsal and anal fin rays are extended and covered with scales. In the aquarium they accustom themselves quite readily to fresh water. A related species, the **Sebae Silverfish** *Monodactylus sebae* [564], grows to a length of 20 cm (8 in) and is found in the tropical sea off West Africa, although it swims quite happily up into the fresh waters of rivers. In spite of its bizarre shape it has never found much popularity.

On the coasts of southern Asia, the East Indies, and Australia live some five species of the genus *Toxotes* which belongs to the family **Toxotidae.** The **Archerfish,** *Toxotes chatareus* [565], grows to a length of 27 cm (11 in). It spends its life near the surface, has a straight back, and possesses the remarkable ability to shoot down with a jet of water, any insect which approaches within 50 cm (20 in) of the water's surface. In captivity it can be fed on insects. In nature it prefers to live in brackish waters of river estuaries.

The family of Batfishes **(Ephippidae)** consists of marine fishes living in the tropical Indo-Pacific region. The most popular genus of this family as far as aquarists are concerned, is the genus *Platax*. These are extremely inquisitive little fishes which rapidly become accustomed to feeding out of the hand of their keeper. They prefer live food, including small fishes such as Guppies. As long as they are well fed they grow very quickly and their appearance, colouring, body shape, and fin form

gradually changes. One of the most popular sea-water aquarium fishes is the **Round Batfish,** which in nature grows to a length of 1 m (3 ft). This species leads a solitary life and is most common in the waters around the islands of Samoa. Picture 566 shows how the Batfish is freed from parasites by a cleaner fish, the **Blue Streak.** Picture 567 shows a medium-sized **Long-finned Batfish,** *Platax teira*. The adults are distinguished by a very high body and strikingly lengthened abdominal fins.

The **Red-rimmed Batfish** *Platax pinnatus* [568] has, likewise, a remarkable body shape. Its distribution area extends from the Pacific Ocean to South Africa. Fully grown, the Red-rimmed Batfish is 50–60 cm (20–24 in) long [569]. The young are almost completely black with an orange mouth and forehead. Slowly a red rim grows around the dorsal fin and around all the other fins. The young Red-rimmed Batfish is without doubt one of the most beautiful species of fish and has a splendid decorative effect. It is a native of the western Pacific, especially

567

Indonesia. While *Platax orbicularis* and *Platax teira* actively hunt their prey, this species approaches the victim slowly and gently, but so much the more effectively.

The related genus *Chaetodipterus* lives in the Atlantic and Pacific oceans. The **Spadefish**, *Chaetodipterus faber* [570], is restricted to the Atlantic, principally in waters south of Cape Cod down to Rio de Janeiro. This fish is up to 1 m (3 ft) in length and is highly valued for its excellent flesh.

The next family, the Scats and Argus-fishes (**Scatophagidae**), lives in the neighbourhood of the coasts of the Indian and Pacific oceans, especially around southern Asia and northern Australia. The **Scat** or **Argus-fish**, *Scatophagus argus* [571], grows to a length of 30 cm (12 in) and inhabits the tropical waters of the Indo-Pacific region. It lives equally happily in salt, fresh, or brackish waters and feeds voraciously on almost anything edible. In the aquarium it is usually given live food, but it will also take vegetable matter such as algae, lettuce, boiled spinach, and soaked porridge oats. The Scat is always an active fish but behaves in a friendly and peaceable manner towards other species. Its 'wobbly' style of swimming is reminiscent of that of the Angelfishes. Owing to its high metabolic rate it creates a great deal of

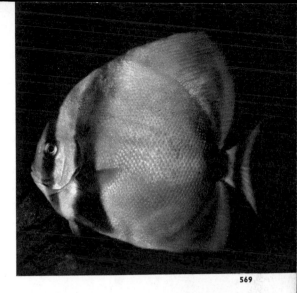

excrement which must be removed from the aquarium with the aid of a fine filter. Adult specimens thrive better in salt water. The **Red Argus** [572] is a subspecies, *Scatophagus argus rubifrons*, which has a red forehead and a red protuberance on the back. Young specimens are spotted and have vertical stripes, while the adults are largely green to brown in colour and eventually take on a uniform tone.

The **Chaetodontidae** (Butterfly-fishes) were formerly arranged by some authorities in several independent families. However, in view of the many features which they have in common the genera and species which follow are considered as members of one single family divided into two subfamilies, **Chaetodontinae** and **Pomacanthinae.** Their striking shape and colouring is a result of their adaptation to life in the coral reefs. Their food consists principally of coral or coral dependent animals and algae. Some species feed on living coral, while others take vegetable remains. Their mouth is generally small and the teeth minute. The body is deep but narrow, enabling the fishes to escape into crevices when threatened. They are marine fishes which inhabit coral reefs. Many genera are known comprising more than 300 species. The best known of these is the genus *Chaetodon* which is widely distributed throughout all the seas of the tropics. The first to be described – by Linnaeus in 1758 – was *Chaetodon capistratus* [573].

571

572

43 Emperor Angelfish *(Pomacanthodes imperator)*

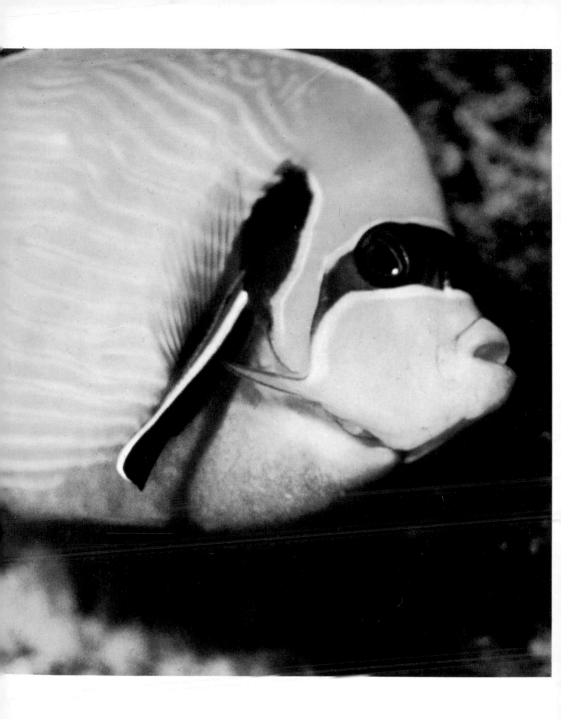

44 Emperor Angelfish with Cleaner Fish (*Labroides dimidiatus*)

Most species of the genus *Chaetodon* are 8–18 cm (3–7 in) when fully grown. They are deservedly popular and are all widely kept in the aquaria of the world.

The **Saddled Butterfly-fish,** *Chaetodon falcula* [574] occurs in Micronesia, Polynesia, and the neighbourhood of the Marshall Islands. It possesses a series of thin vertical stripes and a yellowish

577

basic colouring with a broad stripe across the eyes. When fully grown it has a length of 20 cm (8 in).

The **Red-striped Butterfly-fish,** *Chaetodon lunula* [575], has a distribution extending from the Red Sea to the East Indies, and the Pacific islands as far as Hawaii. This species is particularly common in the neighbourhood of Samoa. Its basic colouring is olive-yellow and it grows to 18 cm (7 in) in length.

Chaetodon chrysurus [Pl. 39] is found in the Indian Ocean from the East African coast to Sumatra. It should be fed on Brine Shrimps in the aquarium if its colouring is to develop fully.

The **Black-backed Butterfly-fish,** *Chaetodon melannotus* [576], has a similar geographical distribution to that of *Chaetodon falcula* although it is mainly found in the East Indies. The basic colouring of this species is dark red-brown which is sometimes almost black. There are twenty-one dark stripes along the sides. The tail is divided into two parts by a vertical yellow stripe the outside of

which is coloured orange, while the inside is blue. The length is 12 cm (5 in).

The **Emperor Butterfly-fish,** *Chaetodontoplus mesoleucus* [577], lives in the coral reefs around Java, Borneo, Celebes, Singapore and the Philippines. It grows to a length of 15 cm (6 in) and it can be kept in exactly the same way as members of the genus *Chaetodon*. However, it more closely resembles members of the genus *Pomacanthus* in the way in which it tackles its food.

The **Butterfly,** *Chaetodon striatus* [578], is a native of the West Indies; it is occasionally caught off Florida. It has several dark stripes across the body and the tail and grows to a length of 15 cm (6 in).

The **Three Striped Butterfly-fish,** *Chaetodon trifasciatus* [579], has a very wide distribution. This fish lives both in the Pacific and Indian Ocean. as well as in the Red Sea. It has an oval-shaped body and a yellow colouring. Of the three vertical stripes one runs across the eyes, the second across

578

the gill covers close behind the eyes, and the third across the tail fin. On the root of the second dorsal fin there is a black spot. Once the Butterfly-fish reaches a length of 15 cm (6 in) it is fully grown. *Chaetodon unimaculatus* [580] ranges from East Africa to Polynesia. This species is characterized

579

by a single dark spot situated almost In the middle of the body. Across the eye there is a dark vertical stripe and a rather less pronounced dark rim covers the rear edge of the dorsal and anal fins. The fish is fully grown when it reaches 13 cm (5 in). The **Criss-cross Butterfly-fish,** *Anisochaetodon*

582

vagabundus [581], is a native of the East Indies.
Its body has a yellow colouring becoming lighter
from the back to the belly. A red stripe crosses the
eyes and a series of further narrow stripes forms
a bizarre pattern on the body. The tail fin is crossed

with a purple band and has an edge of the same
colour. This fish is mature when it reaches a length
of 12 cm (4½ in) although its maximum length is
17 cm (6½ in).
In addition to the already mentioned species of the

583

genus *Chaetodon* there is a number of further species. These are of varying sizes and specimens which are not fully grown are difficult to classify

taxonomically. The individual shown in picture 582, for example, cannot be more closely identified than as a member of the genus *Chaetodon*. The

differences between individuals of the same species can be seen from two photographs of *Parachaetodon ocellatus* [583, 584]. The younger fish [584] has a clearly visible, dark spot at the base of the second dorsal fin; in the older specimen [583] the spot has completely disappeared.

Parachaetodon ocellatus is distributed from the West Indies to Florida. The basic colouring of this fish is silvery yellow with a dark stripe across the eye.

The genus *Prognathodes* is closely related to *Chaetodon*. These fishes have large scales and large gill covers. Only one species, *Prognathodes aculeatus* [585], is known and it inhabits the West Indies. The membrane between the spines of the anterior dorsal fin is deeply serrated.

The subfamily **Pomacanthinae** contains the widely distributed genus *Pomacanthus* (Angelfishes). The **Paru** or **Indian Fish**, *Pomacanthus paru*, which

grows to a length of more than 30 cm (12 in) lives in the waters of the West Indies and Florida. The Paru has a dark colouring with five yellow vertical stripes [586] and is strikingly similar to the **Black Angelfish,** *Pomacanthus arcuatus*. During the course of its growth the shape and colouring of the body

588

589

undergo noticeable changes [587]. The adult Paru [588] is completely black and has extended, pointed processes on the dorsal and anal fins. The teeth [589] are adapted to browsing coral from the reefs.

The **Emperor Angelfish**, *Pomacanthodes imperator*, is surely the most splendidly coloured species and is chiefly found in the East Indies. It grows to a length of 20 cm (8 in). The young are deep blue with a row of concentric, white rings on the body and a complex pattern on the fins [590]. The patterning and colour undergo constant change during its growth to maturity. An adult [Pl. 43] is reddish to purple with about twenty dark yellow stripes which run from the head to the root of the orange tail fin. The Emperor Angelfish readily allows itself to be freed of parasites by the cleaner fish, *Labroides dimidiatus*. *Labroides dimidiatus* not only attends to the outside of the Angelfish but in the larger

species will even reach inside the open mouth and under the gills. Plate 44 shows a mature Emperor Angelfish with its head on one side and its gills held wide open so that the cleaner fish can undertake a thorough cleaning.

The **Ringed Emperor Angelfish**, *Pomacanthodes annularis* [591, Pl. 40], occurs in the Indian Ocean, especially in the neighbourhood of Ceylon. Its colouring is a beautiful bronze with blue stripes on the head, body, and fins, and it has a striking blue-ringed mark behind the head. The tail and pectoral fins are yellow to white. It is mature at a length of 15–30 cm (6–12 in) and the maximum length is 35 cm (14 in).

The **Blue Angelfish**, *Pomacanthodes semicirculatus*, bears a considerable resemblance to the Emperor Angelfish in the changes in colouring which it

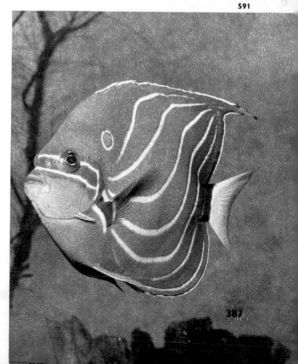

592

593

594

undergoes during development from youth to maturity. It is also similar to the **Isabelita** or **Queen Angelfish,** Angelichthys ciliaris. The young of the Blue Angelfish are at first a dark blue, often almost black, with broad white and turquoise vertical stripes [592, Pl. 41]. A medium-sized specimen at a length of 6–8 cm (2½–3 in) will exhibit a violet colouring with yellow and orange semicircular marks on the middle of the body. This species is common in the neighbourhood of the Seychelles. It grows to a length of 38 cm (15 in). When fully grown it bears a striking resemblance to Pomacanthus paru with its extended dorsal and anal fin [593].

Pomacanthodes chrysurus [Pl. 42] is brightly coloured and reaches a length of 33 cm (13 in). It lives in the western part of the Indian Ocean. It is often imported and kept in sea-water aquaria.

595

596

597

Young specimens of *Pomacanthus maculosus* [594] have a spotted body and are highly decorative. This species is also associated with cleaner fishes, *Labroides dimidiatus* [595].

The genus *Euxiphipops* contains a number of colourful species whose importation has been a source of pleasure to aquarists. *Euxiphipops navarchus* was brought to Europe in 1964. Even in its native surroundings on the coasts of Indonesia and the western Pacific Ocean it is a rare species. It grows to a length of 20 cm (8 in). Its relative the **Yellow-faced Angelfish,** *Euxiphipops xanthometopon* [596], is positively extravagant in the richness of its yellow, orange, blue, and green colouring. It is most familiar in the Gulf of Manhar between India and Ceylon and is only rarely imported. In the aquarium it is notable for its remarkable activity. The **Six-banded Angelfish,** *Euxiphipops sexstriatus* [597], differs from the other species mentioned by the vertical stripes on its body.

The **Rock Beauty,** *Holacanthus tricolor* [598], also shows marked differences between immature and adult specimens. The young are yellow with a dark, blue-ringed spot on the back, whereas the adult fishes, which are up to 60 cm (24 in) long, are orange-yellow in colouring with black sides. Their dorsal and anal fins have a red border. The Rock Beauty lives in the Caribbean Sea.

600

The Butterfly Fishes of the genus *Heniochus* come from the Indian and Pacific Oceans. They live in large shoals and make an impressive effect with their black and white striped bodies and yellow pectoral, dorsal, and tail fins. The elongated fourth fin ray of the dorsal fin is a characteristic feature.

Heniochus acuminatus [599, Pl. 45] reaches a maximum length of about 25 cm (10 in). It is one of the commonest members of the group in the Indian Ocean and the Marshall Islands; it is frequently kept in aquaria.

The **Long-nosed Butterfly Fish**, *Chelmon rostratus* [Pl. 46], lives in the Malayan archipelago and around the Philippines. It is up to 17 cm (6½ in) long and is very difficult to keep in captivity since it feeds only on the tiny shrimps and worms which it finds in the splits and crevices of coral reefs. In the aquarium it is best fed on live Brine Shrimp larvae.

The **Isabelita** or **Queen Angelfish**, *Angelichthys ciliaris* [Pl. 47], undergoes considerable changes in colouring during its growth to maturity. It comes

601

from the West Indies and grows to a length of 60 cm (24 in).

The **Black-and-gold Angelfish,** *Centropyge bicolor* [600], is distributed throughout the waters of India, Melanesia, Micronesia, and Polynesia. The front half of its body and the tail are gold in colouring while the rest is black. Generally it is no longer than 10 cm (4 in).

Centropyge fisheri [601] is most common around the Hawaiian Islands. It is a striking orange colour with a dark-blue spot on the back under the dorsal fin. It measures only 8 cm (3 in).

Centropyge vrolikii [602] is only rarely imported. It is found among the atolls of the Marshall Islands. The brown colouring of the head shades into brownish-red in the middle of the body. The tail,

602

603

604

605

tail fin and anal fin are black. The unpaired fins have a white border and the rear part of the gill-cover is red.

The family **Nandidae** consists of fresh-water fishes from tropical Asia, Africa, and South America. Six genera are known, distinguished by a large dorsal fin and a wide mouth which in some species can be projected forward to a remarkable extent. The lateral line organ is inconspicuous.

Since the beginning of this century aquarists in Europe have bred the **Badis**, *Badis badis* [603], which comes from still waters in India. It grows to a length of 8 cm (3 in) and has a fairly small mouth. In mixed aquaria it is always very peaceable. It requires warm water, about 26–28°C, and usually seeks out hiding places for itself in cavities in rocks, tree roots, or thick tangles of water plants. It will feed on any kind of live foodstuff. During spawning the male adopts a threat posture [604]. The eggs are laid in hollows, stones, or even in a pot prepared for this purpose by the breeder. Picture 605 shows the female digging out a spawning

hole in the gravel at the bottom of the aquarium. The male takes over the care of the fry. In 1936 Ahl described a form with brownish-red colouring and rows of red dots which came from Burma and to which he gave the name *Badis badis burmanicus*.

The **South American Leaf-fish**, *Monocirrhus polyacanthus*, which grows to a length of 8 cm (3 in) comes from the river system of the Amazon and the Rio Negro and from western Guiana. This species has the ability to protrude its mouth far forward and it is an extremely greedy and pugna-cious fish. It is, however, a poor swimmer and camouflages itself by mimicing fallen leaves in the water. It lays its spawn on rocks, large leaves and, in the aquarium, on the glass walls of the tank. The eggs are large and are protected by the male. Picture 606 shows a female with her spawn attached to a tree root. Once the fry reach a certain age they have to be separated since these ravenous fishes will eat their siblings.

The following two genera, *Polycentrus* and *Polycentropsis*, are sometimes arranged in an independent family, **Polycentridae.**

608

Schomburgk's Leaf-fish, *Polycentrus schomburgki*
[607], inhabits the waters of the north-eastern
part of South America and Trinidad. Its length is
in the order of 10 cm (4 in) and the colouring is
attractive. The females are a deep brown, but the
males are velvety-black with turquoise or silver
spots and flecks. Picture 608 shows a pair shortly
before spawning. The male takes up a threatening
posture underneath a leaf. In picture 609 the female
is depositing her spawn on the underside of a leaf
with her belly uppermost — the broad, conical
ovipositor with its stump-like ending is clearly
visible.

The **African Leaf-fish,** *Polycentropsis abbreviata*
[610], comes from the waters of tropical West
Africa. This species grows to a length of 8 cm (3 in)
and is very similar to the South American Leaf-fishes
although the snout reaches even further forward
and is more pointed. The soft parts of the dorsal
and anal fins are short and the colouring variable.
Before spawning it builds a large bubble nest,
preferably under floating leaves. The female lays
up to 100 eggs; after spawning the male takes care
of the offspring. The fry are extremely voracious
and grow quickly, and as long as the water is soft
there are very few losses.

610

The **Cichlidae** are a very large family within the order Perciformes. They are fresh-water fishes and are natives of South and Central America and Africa (there are only two Asiatic species). Some members of this family feed on plants and detritus, while others feed exclusively on plankton and others again are predators. Many species are notable for their particular care of the young. A large number are kept in aquaria and today more than 1,000 separate species are known which are divided into just on 100 genera.

One of the larger genera of Cichlids is *Aequidens*.

45   *Heniochus acuminatus*

46   Long-nosed Butterfly Fish *(Chelmon rostratus)*

47   Queen Angelfish *(Angelichthys ciliaris)*

48 *Cuban Cichlid (Cichlasoma tetracantha)*

611

The **Flag Cichlid**, *Aequidens curviceps* [611], which grows to a length of 8 cm (3 in) lives in the Amazon basin. It is generally a peace-loving fish and can be kept in mixed aquaria except during the spawning season. As a rule the young adults eat their first spawn after one or two days, but thereafter sub-sequent acts of spawning proceed normally and the parents protect the eggs and fry with great solici-tude. The Flag Cichlid is an example of a lithophile species, that is it lays its eggs on stones and rocks. Before spawning the selected stone is carefully cleaned by the parents [612]. Only when this has

612

been done does spawning begin [613]. The female lays the eggs without the male being present; after a short interval the male fertilizes the eggs. The female has a broad ovipositor, while the male has a similar organ which is conical and pointed at the tip. The numerous eggs on the stone grow larger [614] and the male leaves the protection of the eggs to the female [615]. During this period the male swims about in the vicinity of the stone and sees off unwelcome intruders. Concern for

613

614

615

the safety of the nest and offspring are thus under-taken both by the male and the female, who change places at irregular intervals.

Aequidens itanyi comes from deep, still waters in the river Itana in French Guiana. In nature it grows to a length of 14 cm (5½ in). It is one of many species which were first brought live to Europe after 1960 and quickly found popularity among aquarists by reason of their unusual behaviour. They are coloured a delicate pastel green to cinnamon-brown.

The gills are crossed by a light blue mark. The iris of the eyes is golden-green. The intensity of the colouring changes quickly according to the mood of the fish, and both sexes adapt their colouring to the bottom. Spawning takes place in much the same way as in the last-mentioned species. The fe-male [616] takes it in turn with the male to polish a stone clean. The act of spawning and fertilization of the eggs can last for several hours. The female has an unusually broad ovipositor [617] and cor-

respondingly large eggs. Over 400 white eggs may be laid in one batch. The female [618] constantly fans the eggs with her pectoral fins. The fry emerge after forty-two to fifty-six hours at a temperature of 27°C. As soon as they are able to swim freely they feed on living plankton.

Aequidens latifrons [619] has been kept in aquaria since 1906. It comes from Panama and Colombia and grows to a length of 15–20 cm (6–8 in). It has

a high body with five to eight vertical black stripes. In the middle of the scales there is a dark blue or green iridescent spot. The tail fin is a pale to deep wine-red in colour. During the spawning season the colouring increases in intensity. If they are to be kept in the aquarium it must be borne in mind that they grow to a comparatively large size and require correspondingly large quantities of food. The water of the tank must be well filtered and constantly replenished, for this species is very

susceptible to disease. *Aequidens latifrons* spawns several times each year. In spite of its size it neither digs into the bottom nor does it damage the flora around it. As with most Cichlids there are frequent quarrels between the partners The males and females appear to be kissing when they hold each other firmly by the lips [620] but in fact they are biting into each other as they shake from side to side. The female cleans a stone carefully and after this the eggs are laid on the stone, attached to one another in a long string so that they look rather like a pearl necklace. As the eggs begin to

622

increase in size the stone is completely covered by them. The female fans them, not only with her pectoral fins but also with the rhythmic movement of her whole body. Once the fry have emerged and are able to swim independently they surround their parents in a great shoal [621]. If the aquarium is not large enough or is in a position where the parents do not feel sufficiently at ease, it is advisable to remove the young fishes to another tank after a few days so that they do not fall prey to their parents. Adult specimens generally lay a large number of eggs.

625

The **Keyhole Cichlid,** *Aequidens maroni,* is a sociable fish and, except in the spawning season, is well suited for mixed aquaria, although it will sometimes attack the aquarium plants. Spawning takes place on branches or on pieces of wood [623] which can be put into the aquarium as well as upon stones. Adults do occasionally eat their spawn during the first or second spawning, but usually the parent Cichlids can be kept in company with the offspring for a comparatively long period – often longer than six months – for they take intensive care of the young. The two sexes are not markedly different in appearance, but the male [622] normally has longer anal and dorsal fins than the female [624].

The small species of the genus *Apistogramma* are extraordinarily popular as aquarium fishes. **Agassiz' Dwarf Cichlid,** *Apistogramma agassizi,* which comes from the Amazon basin is present both in the river itself and in its tributaries as far upstream as southern Bolivia. It grows to a length of 7–8 cm

(3 in). The males, however, are often larger than this and have a characteristically extended dorsal fin [625]. The colouring is very beautiful, the sides being orange changing to greenish-blue towards the tail. The gill covers have iridescent blue stripes and wavy patterns. Within the tail fin there are orange, blue-green, and black stripes alternating. This fish is very particular about the composition of its water and the siting of the tank. It thrives best in soft water with many hiding places under stones, roots, flowerpots, pieces of wood, and coconut shells. In this species the male, too, protects the nest and spawn.

The **Cockatoo Dwarf Cichlid,** *Apistogramma cacatuoides* [626], comes from Surinam and Guyana. It has a 5–6 cm (2–2½ in) long body with flattened sides. There is a long, dark stripe against a basic olive-brown colouring and a dark spot at the base of the tail fin. The first rays of the dorsal fin are greatly extended and also darker in colour.

626

49 Angelfish *(Pterophyllum scalare)*

50 *Haplochromis burtoni*

Ortmann's Dwarf Cichlid, *Apistogramma ort-manni,* lives in Guyana and the middle region of the Amazon river system. It grows to a length of 7 cm (3 in). The body is greatly compressed at the sides and the colouring varies widely according to the environment. This rather unpopular species requires a water temperature of between 26 and 28°C. Picture 627 shows a female with her spawn attached to the outside of a flowerpot. The female is rather smaller than the male and has a shorter dorsal fin.

Apistogramma pertense [628] lives in the Amazon between Mañaos and Santarem. This fish measures some 5 cm (2 in) although the females are usually somewhat smaller. The colouring varies between

grey and yellow-brown, with a green iridescence; the scales have a darker rim. There is a dark stripe extending from the eye to the root of the tail; the unpaired fins are grey, green, or bluish-green. The soft parts towards the end of the dorsal fin and the anal fin are covered with rows of blue-green and reddish spots. The front part of the dorsal fin is orange and the front edge of the pectoral fin is black in the adult. This species is only rarely kept in aquaria.

The **Yellow Dwarf Cichlid,** *Apistogramma reitzigi* [629], lives in the waters of the central course of the river Paraguay. It is 5 cm (2 in) long. The back is grey-green in colour, the sides yellow-ish-grey and the under-belly is a bright yellow.

629

630

If these fishes are well cared for a bluish iridescence develops on the sides of the bodies. The gill covers below the eyes are covered with a large number of iridescent green spots and stripes. This Dwarf Cichlid is kept in much the same way as *Apistogramma agassizi*. The males often take up a threatening posture [630] and the eggs [631] laid by the female are light red, large, and oval, although they are comparatively few – between forty and seventy – in number. The Yellow Dwarf Cichlid has such a strong parental instinct that the female sometimes guards a shoal of water fleas.

632

633

The most popular species belonging to the genus *Apistogramma* is without doubt **Ramirez' Dwarf Cichlid,** *Apistogramma ramirezi,* which comes from the rivers Apure and Meta in Venezuela. It grows to a length of 5 cm (2 in). Of all species of *Apistogramma* Ramirez's Dwarf Cichlid has the highest, most compressed body. Its basic colouring is a pale purple-red which constantly changes with the direction of the light. The whole body is covered with iridescent green or blue spots; the upper part of the iris has a number of light blue rays and the front part of the dorsal fin is completely black. The front two fin rays of the male [623] are greatly extended. Care and breeding are similar to that of *Apistogramma agassizi.* Spawning normally takes place over a stone [633] although a sandy depression will also serve. Both parents take it in turns to watch over the spawn. This fish has a very beautiful colouring but does not live long, seldom reaching a greater age than two years. It is susceptible to numerous diseases, including ascites or *Ichthyophonus.* Recently an albino form with red eyes has been bred [634] but it is not remotely comparable in beauty with the original form.

Apistogramma trifasciatum [635] inhabits the Amazon river system. In addition to the nominal form a subspecies is also known, *Apistogramma trifasciatum haraldschultzi.* The males are up to 5 cm (2 in) long but the females only measure 4 cm (1½ in). These fishes are rarely kept in aquaria for they are not very fertile. One spawning gives rise to only forty to eighty young. Unlike many other Cichlids *Apistogramma trifasciatum* does not always form lasting pair bonds: instead the male marks out territory in which there are several females in various stages of caring for their young. The females are quite aggressive to one another and take great pains to protect their own little territory. Once the fry are able to fend for themselves the females swim round the shoal of young fishes and sometimes move into the territory of another male.

One of the largest of the Cichlids is the **Oscar's** or **Velvet Cichlid,** *Astronotus ocellatus,* [636], which lives in the waters of the Amazon, the Parana, the Paraguay, and the Rio Negro. It is up to 35 cm (14 in) long and has beautiful colouring, especially

635

when young, being decorated with coffee-brown, black-rimmed spots. As it grows larger it changes its colouring to a rather less interesting grey-brown. If it is to be kept in the aquarium its length must be borne in mind, especially since the larger specimens are very unsociable and require large quantities of live food, especially meal worms and house crickets. One spawning results in more than

636

1,000 young which, during the first few days, hang from the sides of their parents' body, where they receive not only protection but possibly also their first food.

Cichlids of the genus *Cichlasoma* reach comparatively large proportions. The **Jack Dempsey**, *Cichlasoma biocellatum* [637], has been kept in aquaria since 1904. It comes from the Amazon and Negro rivers and is up to 18 cm (6½ in) long. Its basic colouring ranges from fawn to dark brown or black and there are seven or eight pronounced vertical stripes of irregular size on the sides of the body. Each scale has an iridescent blue point and the dorsal fin has a red border. During the spawning season these fishes are aggressive and unsociable

638

[638]. They require an aquarium without water plants: if present they are quickly destroyed by the constant burrowings of the adults. From each act of spawning about 700–800 young arise. The Jack Dempsey is a very long lived species achieving an age of five years and more.

The **Barred** or **Flag Cichlid**, *Cichlasoma festivum* [639], lives in the waters of western Guiana and the river system of the Amazon. It is about 15 cm (6 in) long. Sexual dimorphism during the spawning season is most noticeable owing to the change in form of the ovipositor. According to the literature

639

on the subject this fish is a peaceful and reticent inhabitant of the aquarium and does not destroy plant growth. During the spawning season, however, the adult fishes wreak havoc in the tank and usually very little is left of the plant growth. Picture 640 shows a fish preparing a spawning place. This is undertaken with such vigour that the female does not hesitate to move quite large logs if they lie in the way of her chosen bed. After this hectic preparation the act of spawning itself takes place comparatively peacefully on a stone [641] or on a flowerpot. Both adults take great care of their spawn from the outset and carefully remove the white, unfertilized eggs which are beginning to decay in order that they shall not infect the remaining healthy eggs. The frequent failures in breeding can generally be attributed to improper feeding. About one week after the fry start to swim independently they should be carefully fed with finest powdered food – preferably rotifers. If they are fed on *Cyclops* nauplii up to ninety per cent of the fry will die during the first two or three days.

The colouring of the **Fire-mouth Cichlid,** *Cichlasoma meeki,* is very vivid. This fish comes

640

from the waters of Guatemala and Yucatan. It is up to 15 cm (6 in) long, its body is deep and it has an arched back. The basic colouring is grey-blue with a violet iridescence. The back is darker while the belly is olive-green to orange, and the throat and lower jaw are a most attractive brick-red.

641

The sides are striped with five to seven vertical lines of differing size and intensity of colouring; the scales have a red edge so that the body seems to have a criss-cross pattern. The dorsal fin has a blue border, while that of the anal fin is black. The males may be distinguished by extended dorsal and tail fins. Some specimens take up an exagger-

ated threatening posture in which the gills are raised. The Fire-mouth Cichlid is not particularly aggressive except in the spawning season, when it usually shows extraordinary activity and often attacks smaller members of the same species. A pair which has achieved harmony spawns readily. Picture 642 shows a pair inside a flowerpot. They

spend many hours deciding whether this home will be suitable for their numerous progeny. (At long last, the flowerpot, in this case, was approved as suitable.) The eggs are protected by both parents together. In picture 643 the male is on duty. In another case where spawning has taken place on a stone [644] a female is removing the white, infertile eggs. These present great dangers to the continued development of the fertilized eggs since fungus can infect and destroy the whole brood. Once the fry emerge they remain in the protective company of the parents [645] for several days. The most suitable temperature for breeding is 24°C.

646

The **Zebra** or **Convict Cichlid,** *Cichlasoma nigrofasciatum* [646], comes from lakes Atitlan and Amatitlan in Guatemala and elsewhere in Central America. It grows to a length of 8–10 cm (3–4 in) and is dark brown to bluish in colour on its back with mouse-grey sides and sometimes a violet iridescence. It acquires its name from the eight or nine vertical stripes, the intensity of which depends on the fishes' general well-being and environment. The fins are metallic green in colouring. The male has extended dorsal and anal fins, while the female can be easily recognized in that she is smaller than the male and has a bronze-coloured under-belly. The Convict Cichlid is a very attractive species, but unfortunately it is always very aggressive both towards members of the same species and other fishes. In the aquarium it constantly stirs up and digs into the bottom; it cannot be kept with water plants since it not only digs them up, but also eats them. This fish can be fed on lettuce leaves, soaked porridge oats, and algae amongst other things. Convict Cichlids take care of their spawn and fry in much the same way as the preceding species but are even more concerned to find

hiding places in recesses in stones, flowerpots, etc.
After spawning the female watches over the eggs
[647] and the parents attempt to hide their offspring
as soon as they emerge in carefully prepared sandy
beds between the stones on the tank floor. The
adults carry their young about from one place to
another, especially when they are disturbed or
suspect that their first hiding place has been discovered. This removal takes place with great secrecy
and often one of the parents will attempt to distract
the attention of the observer by some unrelated
and very noticeable activity, such as digging a hole
under a stone, while the other slips away between
the rocks carrying the offspring with it. The young
can be left in the company of their parents for
a long period. Picture 648 shows a female with
offspring which have reached a size of about 2 cm
(1 in).

An albino form of *Cichlasoma nigrofasciatum* has
been artificially bred in captivity and in a darkened
tank its milk-white colouring has a striking effect.
Nevertheless it has not enjoyed much popularity
until now.

649

The **Banded Cichlid**, *Cichlasoma severum* [649], lives in the northern part of the Amazon river system and in Guiana. It is up to 20 cm (8 in) long and its body is deep, almost oval with much compressed sides. In colouring one specimen will differ widely from the next depending on the place of origin and the environment in which it is kept. Its basic colouring is copper-yellow, brown, green, or even completely black; each scale carries a reddish-brown spot. The pattern on the body is in the form of vertical stripes of variable intensity. The abdominal fins are reddish-brown to black and the iris of the eye is blood-red. The female is generally lighter in colouring and has shorter dorsal and anal fins. In spite of its size this fish is popular among aquarists and is frequently encountered in captivity. Except during the spawning season it is peaceful and does no great damage to the plants and equipment of the aquarium. However, during the spawning season it chases other fishes and must be transferred to a tank without water plants. It is kept in much the same way as *Cichlasoma festivum*. One act of spawning gives rise to more than 1,000 eggs. This is a warmth-loving species and even in winter the temperature must not be allowed to sink below 22°C.

One of the largest South American Cichlids is *Cichlasoma spilurum* [650]. Among European aquarists this species first came into prominence in about 1964. It was originally thought to spawn in holes and recesses, however it has since been established that it will spawn in flowerpots, on the outer wall of the aquarium or on stones, roots, and elsewhere. If the parents are frightened they take up a position in front of their spawn as if they intend to cover it with their bodies [651]. Older males have a characteristic hump on the top of the head.

The **Cuban Cichlid**, *Cichlasoma tetracantha* [Pl. 48], is likewise up to 20 cm (8 in) long. Its colouring is extraordinarily variable although the basic hue is always grey-green. This fish is an inhabitant of still and flowing waters, both fresh and brackish, in Cuba and Barbados. It digs out a dish-shaped spawning bed in shallow places and requires the high temperature of 27–30°C for successful spawning. Although it is usually an attractively coloured fish it is not popular among aquarists owing to its aggressive and antisocial nature.

The genus *Geophagus*, Earth Eaters, is characterized by a deep body, compressed at the sides. Its members are aggressive and constantly dig up the bed of the aquarium. Some of them protect their young in much the same way as species of *Cichlasoma*, while others are mouthbrooders, or alternatively

take their young into the mouth when there is danger. They are found throughout the tropics of South America as far south as the river Plate.

Of the many imported species the most common is *Geophagus jurupari* [652]. It lives mainly in sandy-bottomed waters in the Amazon basin and Guiana.

652

653

51 *Nannochromis dimidiatus*

52a Pelmatochromis kribensis
52b Pelmatochromis thomasi

It grows to a length of 3 cm (9 in) and lives in shoals. In spite of its hostile expression it is in fact a peace-loving fish and does not even attack water plants, provided that they are protected above the roots by a glass plate or large stones. This species likes warmth and requires a temperature of 25–28°C for breeding. It is transitional between those Cichlids which hide their offspring in holes and the mouthbrooders, for the adults only occasionally take their young into the mouth during the first fourteen days of their life.

The 8 cm (3 in) long **Golden-eyed Dwarf Cichlid,** *Nannacara anomala*, occurs in Guyana. The male [653] has green sides, with a metallic iridescence and a triangular mark on each scale. The adult fishes prefer aquaria with thick plant growth and many recesses beneath stones, roots, etc. They will only take live food, especially mosquito larvae and worms. With the exception of the spawning season they are sociable both with one another and with other species. They lay their eggs on carefully cleaned and polished stones [654]. After spawning the male should be removed lest his presence, in the confined space of the tank, disturb the female. Only the female tends the nest and

during this period her body takes on a hatched or criss-cross pattern [655]. The young emerge after two to three days and are taken by the female

to previously prepared depressions in the bottom: only after a further five days are they able to swim independently. The female keeps her characteristic body pattern, which is of varying intensity, for as long as she is protecting her free-swimming young [656]. At first the young feed on plankton, which should be given in small quantities several times a day. The breeder's attention is really only required during the first few days; thereafter the little fishes are quite hardy and lively, although the water temperature must be kept at 24–25°C. Picture 657

shows the typical pattern on a young specimen which has reached the length of 2 cm (1 in).

The Cichlids belonging to the genus *Pterophyllum* lay their eggs on strong, broad leaves of water plants. The **Deep Angelfish**, *Pterophyllum altum* [658], which has very high dorsal and anal fins and a head with a saddle-like depression above the mouth, is sometimes imported from the area of the Orinoco river. However, it is apparently not at present kept in European aquaria.

657

658

The **Scalare** or **Angelfish,** *Pterophyllum scalare* [Pl. 49], whose home is in the middle course of the Amazon and its tributaries is, by contrast, very common in European aquaria. Since it has a wide geographical area of distribution quite a number of forms and colour variations occur among which the most common, known as *Pterophyllum eimekei,* is also bred in captivity. It has short fins and a powerful body; adult specimens have a cushion of fat — especially prominent in the males — on the forehead. That *Pterophyllum eimekei* is not a separate species was proved by L. P. Schultz in 1967 as a result of investigations into specimens taken from both nature and aquaria. Today, therefore,

659

all artificially bred Scalares must be regarded as belonging to the species *Pterophyllum scalare*. When they are about 15 cm (6 in) long their span from the tip of the dorsal fin to the tip of the anal fin is some 26 cm (10 in). They require the comparatively warm water temperature of 22–24°C and if there are not to be losses from among the eggs and newly emerged fry, the water temperature must be raised to 27–32°C for breeding. If the temperature drops below 20°C the adults become susceptible to infections of the eye. This disease can generally be successfully treated by quickly raising the temperature as high as 35°C and ensuring a plentiful supply of oxygen in the water.

660

However, the fishes are very sensitive and react unpredictably to chemicals and medication. Scalares feed on larger aquatic invertebrates, for example worms, water fleas, the larvae of mosquitoes, water beetles, and dragonflies and thrive best on a varied diet. Over a period of time a number of variations have been bred, among which the Black Scalare [659] is very rare since only a small proportion of the fry come out black, the rest reverting to the original colouring. A similar phenomena can be observed in the case of the **Black Veiled Scalare** [660]. The **Smoky Scalare** [661] and the **Veiled Scalare** [662] are purer artificial forms and genetically more stable. As

662

has already been mentioned all Scalares spawn, on the leaves of water plants (*Cryptocoryne*, *Echinodorus*): these should then be gently transferred to a specially prepared breeding tank, for Scalares take no great care of their offspring, at any rate in captivity. One act of spawning can give rise to upwards of 1,000 eggs. If the newly emerged young fall to the bottom of the aquarium they quickly die. The fry emerge after twenty-four to thirty-six hours at a temperature of 27–30°C. Requisites for successful development for the eggs and the fry are a high temperature, a plentiful supply of oxygen, and crystal clear water. To prevent decaying unfertilized eggs from infecting the others it is generally sufficient to use a weak solution of fungicide. After emerging the fry continue to feed for a few days on the yolk sac and not until several days later do the young fishes swim independently and start to take food. If there is a rich supply of food and a suitable water temperature the young grow astonishingly quickly since they are able to digest incredible quantities of food. In the Prague Botanical Gardens a group of young Scalares took three months to grow to a length of 10 cm (4 in) in a tank which was planted with *Victoria regia* and had a steady water temperature of 35°C.
Of all the Cichlids those most in demand are the species and subspecies of the genus *Symphysodon*.

The only one of these which is widely bred in aquaria is the so-called **Brown Discus**, *Symphysodon aequifasciata axelrodi* [663], which comes from the waters of Brazil and grows to a length of 12–15 cm (4½–6 in). It is less striking in colouring than its relatives the **Green Discus**, *Symphysodon aequifasciata aequifasciata*, and the **Blue Discus**, *Symphysodon aequifasciata haraldi*. These fishes are extremely difficult to keep and to breed since they are very particular throughout life about the composition of the water and the nature of their food. Furthermore, they are frequent victims of several incurable diseases and the young can be brought to maturity only with the greatest difficulty. For the first few days after they begin to swim freely the fry feed on a secretion in the skin of the parents, and only later do they start to take live plankton. If the parents do not secrete this substance at the right time their offspring are condemned to death: after several hours, or at the most a couple of days, the entire brood dies. Picture 664 shows a Brown Discus pair with their young. It has been possible in captivity to cross the **Brown Discus** with the original **Discus**, *Symphysodon discus*; the hybrid appears to be hardier and more fertile than the original form. The original species [665] comes from the Rio Negro and its tributaries. It is up to 20 cm (8 in) long and it always

665

commands a high price, for it has only rarely been successfully bred in captivity, and aquarists throughout the world are dependent on imports from its native waters. In the United States it is known as 'king of the aquarium fishes' owing to its bright colouring, especially the contrasting red and blue, wavy, longitudinal stripes.

The Chromides (genus *Etroplus*) come from India and South-East Asia. The **Orange Chromide,** *Etroplus maculatus* [666], lives in the fresh and estuarine waters of western India and Ceylon. It has

been known in Europe since 1905. This species grows to a length of 8 cm (3 in) and has a bluish-green to dark brown back with orange to gold sides on which are situated three large, round, dark brown blotches with a bluish or yellow border. The Orange Chromide is very sensitive to sudden changes in the water and is frequently attacked by parasitic diseases, especially by Ichthyophthiriasis. Its resistance to disease is improved by the addition of a little sea water (one or two tablespoonfuls for every ten litres of water). The adult fish will not survive a drop in the water temperature below

25°C. Reproduction and breeding take place in much the same way as among previously described phytophile Cichlids. Both parents take part in watching over the offspring. The young feed in much the same way as the Discus, on a secretion of the parents skin, but they can also be reared separately from their parents since they will feed straight away on plankton.

A related species, the **Green Chromide**, *Etroplus suratensis* [667], lives in brackish water in Ceylon.

It is significantly larger than other Chromides and in nature it grows to a length of 40 cm (16 in). Its basic colouring is grey-green to bluish-green with a fine mother-of-pearl iridescence throughout the body and six to eight vertical stripes on the sides. It can only be kept for a short time in fresh water, but on the other hand, unadulterated sea water is also unacceptable although the intensity of the colouring improves. It loves warmth and the water temperature should not on any account be allowed

667

668

to sink below 23°C. It has been kepte in Eropu since 1905 but has not apparently been successfully bred.

Members of the genus *Haplochromis* are true mouthbrooders. The **Small** or **Egyptian Mouth-** **brooder,** *Haplochromis multicolor* [668], is found throughout Africa, particularly in the lower course of the Nile. It grows to a length of 7 cm (3 in). The body of this fish is gold, green, or blue. It is peaceable and suitable for mixed aquaria and can be kept with other species as long as they are not

too small. Shortly after spawning takes place the pair dig a hole in the sand in which the female then lays her eggs: these are promptly fertilized by the male [669]. After spawning the female gathers up the eggs in her mouth and holds them in a pouch beneath her throat. At this point the male should be removed from the tank so that he does not disturb the female unnecessarily. The fry take ten to twenty days, depending on the water temperature, to emerge within the brood pouch of the female, and only when they leave it does the female begin to take food again. However, for at least another week the young fishes constantly swim back to the security of their mother's mouth, especially at night or if they are threatened. The adult fishes will not tolerate a water temperature lower then 20°C and for breeding this must be 25–26°C.

The somewhat larger *Haplochromis burtoni* is up to 12 cm (5 in) long. It lives in the tropical waters of East and central Africa, especially in Bahr el Djebel, Semliki, the Albert Nile, Lake Albert, Lake George, Lake Edward, the Ruwenzori region and the waters of Lake Chad and the Nile itself. In contrast to the last-mentioned species it lays its eggs on flat stones or on pieces of slate. Picture 671 shows the preparations for the act of spawning. During the courtship display, especially if the eggs of the female are not yet ready to be laid, the pair may fight. For this reason it is as well to prepare a number of recesses and hiding places in the

670

aquarium, preferably among stones, into which the female can retire for a while [670]. The water temperature should be in the order of 27°C during spawning.

671

439

672

673

Before the female expels her eggs the male lies
down on his side on a carefully cleaned stone,
bends himself into a semicircle and begins to quiver
violently with his whole body and fins as he ejacu-
lates the sperm. In the meantime the female places
her mouth close to his anal fin which [Pl. 50]
strikingly resembles the eggs with its orange spots,
and takes the sperm of the male into her mouth.
Then she lays her eggs on a stone and takes these,
too, into her brood pouch. It is not uncommon for
the male to then undergo a second ejaculation,
and if so the female will repeat the performance of
taking the sperm into her mouth. The whole
spawning process lasts for about one and a half
hours. This species protects its progeny in much
the same way as other Cichlids. These fishes should
be well fed on tubifex worms, mosquito larvae, etc.
Haplochromis polystigma [672] has been imported
only rarely of late. This species comes from the
lakes of Africa, especially Lake Nyasa and Lake
Nkata. Further information about its habits and
breeding is not available.

Another genus of African Cichlid is *Hemichromis*.
The **Jewelfish** or **Red Cichlid**, *Hemichromis
bimaculatus*, is encountered in large numbers in the
Niger, the Nile, and the Congo. It grows to a length
of 15 cm (6 in) and has an olive to grey-brown
back with yellowish-green sides and light yellow
under-belly. During the spawning season this is
one of the most beautiful of African Cichlids. The
male is dark red with small iridescent, green spots.

676

The front part of the belly of the female is yellow and the rear part pink. Spawning takes place on a stone and in order to clean this the female often takes a vertical position with her head downwards [673]. In this species, too, spawning takes place as described above. Picture 674 shows the female at the moment of laying her eggs, while in picture 675 both partners are together – the ovipositor is clearly visible. Older specimens must be kept in isolated pairs since they are very unsociable. However, they take great care of their young. In spite of their aggressiveness they have been widely reared in Europe since 1907.

Less popular is the **Banded Jewelfish** or **Five-spot Cichlid,** Hemichromis fasciatus [676], which comes from central West Africa. It is up to 30 cm (12 in) long. The Banded Jewelfish is yellow green with a bronze iridescence and has five large, glossy, black, oval patches on the side of the body. Older specimens have a brick-red dot on each scale. The mouth is large and wide. Care and breeding are as for the species described above.

The adult fishes usually dig into the floor of the aquarium and they feed only on live food, preferring large fragments of meat, water insects, and worms. They protect and accompany their offspring until the latter have reached a size of 2–3 cm (1 in).

The genus Herichthys consists of Central and South American Cichlids; its distribution stretches further north than that of other Cichlids. Some authors regard Herichthys as a close relative of the genus Cichlasoma. Among aquarists the **Texas Cichlid,** Herichthys cyanoguttatus, is very popular. It has a high back and lives in north-east Mexico and the southern states of the USA, especially in the Rio Grande del Norte and its tributaries. In the aquarium it grows to a length of 15 cm (6 in). Its whole body is covered with small iridescent blue-green spots on a dark grey-green background. The female is generally smaller than the male. This species is aggressive and damages water plants by its constant burrowing in the floor of the aquarium. It is sensitive to dirty water and can be poisoned by excessive accumulations of organic matter. It is,

therefore, recommended that about one-third of the water in the aquarium should be changed regularly. Picture 678 shows a male, which can be distinguished from the female by its flattened belly and extended dorsal and anal fins. The full face view of the Texas Cichlid [677] suggests pugnacity. *Nannochromis* is a genus of African Cichlids with small, thin bodies. The males often have a flat or even receding belly which makes them look underfed: the lines of the female are fuller.

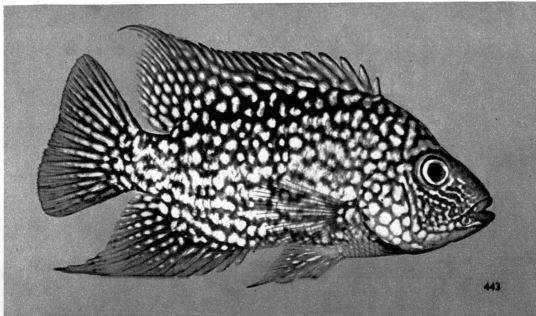

679

Nannochromis nudiceps [679] comes from the Congo river system. It is kept and bred in much the same way as members of the genera *Apistogramma* and *Pelmatochromis*. As a rule the female is very active in the care of the offspring. These fishes dig holes in the bottom between stones, roots, flowerpots, or coconut shells, in order to lay their spawn. The fry grow slowly and the female only spends a short time caring for them. It is possible to rear the young without their parents.

A relative of this species, *Nannochromis dimidiatus* [Pl. 51], has only rarely been imported; it is extremely difficult to rear in captivity. The males are generally very active and it is necessary at first to separate them from the females, for example by a sheet of glass, in order that they may get used to one another. Furthermore, success in breeding is dependent on a whole number of factors, for example temperature, water composition, and even the internal arrangement of the aquarium in which the adults have to feel assured of the safety of their progeny.

A large number of African Cichlids belonging to the genus *Pelmatochromis* are bred by aquarists. In nature they live in the waters of West Africa, especially in river mouths or meanders and in a variety of lagoons and pools near the coast. They live in shallow water with a thick growth of water plants or water-logged wood and roots. In comparison with other Cichlids they can be described as being extremely peaceful, although during the spawning season some species dig into the bed without, however, doing very much harm to well-rooted plants. They prefer a slight salt content to the water (one or two teaspoonfuls of salt to every ten litres of water is sufficient).

53a 'Turquoise-gold Cichlid' *(Pseudotropheus auratus)*
53b *Labeotropheus fuelleborni*

54   *Pseudotropheus* zebra

Pelmatochromis annectens [680] is found in all fresh and brackish waters from Liberia to Nigeria. The male is up to 10 cm (4 in) long, the female somewhat smaller. The best results in breeding have been observed in pairs which have chosen each other and separated themselves from a shoal of young fishes kept together. They prefer to spawn in flowerpots or coconut shells lying on their sides. Picture 681 shows a female laying her eggs on the underside of an overhang while the male

682

looks on. In picture 682 the male is fertilizing the spawn. As a rule both parents watch over their offspring. The eggs are about the size of grains of millet and are light brown. The fry emerge some three days after fertilization and thereafter grow extremely quickly. Picture 683 shows the pattern on a young specimen about 3 cm (1 in) long. This species is warmth loving but will survive a fairly large drop in temperature for a short time. It can, if necessary, be fed on dried food.

Pelmatochromis kribensis is a very popular species. It lives in the tropical waters of Africa, especially in the Niger delta. The male grows to a length of

683

about 9 cm (3½ in), the female only 7 cm (3 in).
This beautifully coloured fish has a brownish back
and blue to purple iridescent sides. The male
obviously differs from the female in the form of the
tail fin [684] which is arrow shaped and has between
one and five dark spots with a light yellow border
on its upper edge. The hind part of the underneath
is wine-red to violet [Pl. 52a] and the anal fin is
triangular.

In order to breed this species a water temperature
of 25–28°C is necessary. Both partners watch over
the spawn and the reddish-brown eggs are most
often laid in a flowerpot put into the aquarium:
if the adults cannot find enough natural hiding
places they will dig hollows under stones or between plant roots for this purpose. It is advisable to
transfer the eggs to a glass tank with gently aerated
water. The fry emerge after two to three days
and after a further four to five days are quite independent. They are unsociable towards one another
and it is best to keep individual pairs separately.

Pelmatochromis guentheri [685], which grows to
a length of 16 cm (6 in), lives in West Africa between
Ghana and Gabon. The females are generally smaller than the males. The basic colouring of this
fish is olive-green with a blue iridescence, while
the back is darker. The dorsal fin has a shimmering
longitudinal stripe with a blood-red edge, the tail
fin is yellowish with red marks and stripes on the
upper edge. This species, too, is unsociable and
should therefore be kept only in pairs. In addition

it is voracious and not very choosy about its
food. Like some other members of this genus, it
is a mouthbrooder, and both parents take care
of their offspring, exchanging the eggs from mouth
to mouth until the young fishes emerge. Picture
686 shows two specimens in the characteristic
threat posture with gills raised which is the usual
preliminary to spawning.

686

687

Pelmatochromis klugei [687] comes from Nigeria and was first described by Meinken in 1960. Its appearance and way of life are similar to that of *Pelmatochromis kribensis* that even the author of the original scientific description came to the conclusion that this was in fact a subspecies, which he named *Pelmatochromis kribensis klugei*. Questions concerning the classification and relations between the species of this genus cannot be said to have been finally settled. However, these Cichlids are not difficult to breed. They feed on *Cyclops*, water fleas, mosquito larvae, whiteworms, and small earthworms, and in addition they continually consume detritus. They prefer shady aquaria with plenty of hiding places and a water temperature of 24–28°C.

The **Emerald Cichlid,** *Pelmatochromis taeniatus* [688], lives in the Niger delta and the lower course of the Calabar. The male is 9 cm (3½ in) long and the female only about 7 cm (3 in). It resembles in body form *Pelmatochromis kribensis*. However, the mark on the under-belly of the female is not red but emerald green. A broad olive-brown stripe runs from the front of the head to the root

of the tail: in the male this is often broken up into a dotted line or disappears entirely. The pelvic fins of the female are emerald green as is her belly. The tail fin is orange above and green below in the male, uniformly orange in the female.

Pelmatochromis thomasi was introduced from Sierra Leone to the aquaria of Europe fairly recently. Externally it resembles the species *Apistogramma ramirezi*. The brilliance of its colouring is almost unbelievable. Adult males [Pl. 52b] are sometimes grey-green and have an iridescent blue mark on every scale. There are three dark patches or lines, one on the gill covers, the second about the middle of the body, and the third at the root of the tail. Altogether there can be up to seven vertical stripes, of which the first runs straight over the eyes. The dorsal fin has a red border with a golden sheen extending to the upper edge of the tail fin. The dorsal and anal fins of the male are high with elongated rays; his pelvic fins have a blue or black border on the leading edge. Their eggs are a light grey-green and are laid on a carefully cleaned stone. In picture 689 the male is seen busily cleaning a flat stone for this purpose. The next picture

689

The genus *Tilapia* belongs among the plant-eating Cichlids. Its members have a comparatively short, deep body which is covered with cycloid or ctenoid scales. The teeth are arranged in two or more rows. Various individual species live in Africa and the Middle East. Several of them are mouthbrooders.

Tilapia brevimanus comes from Guinea. This fish is about 15 cm (6 in) long. It has yellowish-green colouring with grey-green to black vertical stripes, and it feeds on a wide variety of water plants which it prefers to every other foodstuff. *Tilapia brevimanus* spawns in depressions in the sand, and in the aquarium it will dig out flat saucer-shaped hollows. Its eggs are dark green in colour and it lays them in groups, preferably directly on to the glass wall of the tank [692]. Both parents take care of the young, and breeding and rearing are extremely simple.

The **Big-head Mouthbrooder**, *Tilapia macrocephala* [693], lives in fresh and brackish waters from Ghana to Nigeria. It is 17 cm (6½ in) long and has a rather dull, yellow-green colouring. The pelvic fins are a misty dark brown to violet, while the throat is often black and the lips white or off-white. After spawning the male carries the eggs in his mouth: little else is known about the breeding of this unsociable and pugnacious fish. This species only feeds on small fragments, preferably water fleas, tubifex worms, and midge larvae. It does not destroy plants but occasionally eats dead plant matter and it readily removes the algae from the walls of the aquarium.

[690] shows the female after laying her eggs, while the male stays close to her. Breeding of this undemanding Cichlid requires a water temperature of only 23–25°C; about 500 young may result from one spawning. Their growth can be speeded up by increasing the water temperature. At 28°C the fry emerge after only forty-eight hours and after a further three days they are already swimming independently. The typical colouring of the young fish at a length of about 2.5 cm (1 in) is shown in picture 691.

690

The **Mozambique Mouthbrooder,** *Tilapia mossambica*, lives in fresh and brackish waters in East Africa. In nature it grows to a length of 36 cm (12 in) but in the aquarium it only reaches 12–14 cm ($4\frac{1}{2}$–$5\frac{1}{2}$ in). It is silvery-grey, sometimes with a tinge of green or blue, but during the spawning season the males become an intensive blue or blue-black in colouring. This fish feeds on live food, but will not reject dried food or vegetable remains. The eggs are laid in small funnel-shaped depressions. In picture 694 the female is digging out such a depression while the male looks on. After spawning the female takes the eggs into her mouth and holds them in the broodpouch, where they remain until the fry emerge. The eggs are orange coloured and transparent at first; later a dark spot – the eye of the new fish – appears. After emerging the young leave the mouth of the mother to seek food. At first they return after a few minutes but as they grow bigger they take longer excursions and eventually leave the protection of their mother's mouth. For this reason the mother is constantly

with her brood during the first few days [695]. Only later do the young fish go further away from her in the search for food and at the slightest sign of danger they flee back to their mother to seek protection there [696]. Picture 697 shows the last of the young fishes seeking admission in vain. One act of spawning gives rise to more than 300 young, which hatch in ten to twelve days.

In recent years the Cichlids from Lakes Tanganyika and Nyasa – in particular the brightly coloured species of the genera *Tropheus*, *Labeotropheus*, and *Pseudotropheus* – have aroused much interest. Picture 698 shows a male of the species *Tropheus*

duboisi. Observations by the German aquarist Chlupaty have ascertained that the female spawns in the open water above the bottom and immediately after expelling the eggs turns like lightning and takes them in her mouth. The young are a deep black with white spots which are arranged in rows on the head, the body, and the fins.

Labeotropheus trewavasae is a fish with a long body. More than half of the females are coloured orange with dark or black spots [699], while the others have vertical stripes. The brightly coloured males have a radiant blue body, head, and tail, with a reddish-brown dorsal fin [Pl. 55a]. *Labeotropheus*

fuelleborni. [Pl 53b] feeds principally on algae found on rocks and reefs. This Cichlid is about 12 cm (4½ in) long and the adults have a low-set mouth pulled down at the corners which extends over the whole width of the head. Like the preceding species the females are both striped and spotted.

Pseudotropheus zebra [Pl. 54], likewise, prefers to live in crevasses among the rocks. It adapts itself easily to captivity and not only eats algae but appears to be almost omnivorous. It is very aggressive towards smaller fishes, and in nature marks out an extensive territory. For this reason it can only be reared in large tanks.

The '**Turquoise-gold Cichlid**', *Pseudotropheus auratus* [Pl. 53a], is very striking both by reason of its colouring and the pattern. Its body possesses black and yellow longitudinal stripes and the upper part of the tail fin has a row of black marks. In the aquarium it will feed not only on algae but also on water fleas and tubifex worms. This species, too, is a mouthbrooder. Not until they are fully developed and 1 cm (½ in) long do the young fishes leave the mouth of their mother. Each brood is comparatively small in number, there being between six and forty individuals.

698

The **Lemon-yellow Cichlid,** *Lamprologus leleupi* [700], is one of the smallest of the Cichlids from Lake Tanganyika. Its basic colouring is lemon-yellow to orange, while the fins have a rim of shimmering blue. Like the species last described, this fish lives in clefts in the rocks. For this reason it requires a stony bed to the aquarium. Besides plant remains it will also feed on the larvae of phantom midges, small snails, etc. It lays its eggs in holes in piles of stones, usually up to 150 eggs at a time. The fry emerge after three days and after about ten days begin to take food. They prefer Brine Shrimps *(Artemia)*. The Lemon-yellow Cichlid grows comparatively slowly and is very particular about the cleanliness and nitrate content of the water.

699

The family **Pomacentridae** (Demoiselles) are characterized by a short body which is often very deep and compressed at the sides. Members of this family live in the tropical parts of the Indian, Pacific and Atlantic Oceans, mainly around coral reefs. The family contains fifteen genera with almost 200 species. They are particularly lively and brightly coloured; as they grow older the colouring alters. Some anatomical features point to an evolutionary relationship with the family Labridae, others to the family Kyphosidae, and still others perhaps to the Cichlidae. These fishes are quite popular in aquaria, where some have been success-

fully bred. Some of the most common genera are *Abudefduf*, *Dascyllus*, *Pomacentrus*, *Eupomacentrus*, *Amphiprion*, *Chromis*, and *Heliases*. A number of other genera have been brought to Europe and are also kept in the USA. Picture 701 shows a species of *Chromis* beside a sea anemone. It has a deeply indented tail fin.

The **Anemone-fishes** of the genus *Amphiprion* are easy to keep. According to Wickler and de Graaf all these species live in the tentacles of large sea anemones (*Discosoma* or *Stoichactis*) and are in no way affected by the poison contained in their

702

tentacles although it has a fatal effect on other fishes. If the Anemone-fish approaches the tentacles of the anemone the latter does not exude its poison, a fact which so far has not been satisfactorily explained, although it has been suggested that mucus secreted by the fish prevents the discharge of the

anemone's stinging cells. All species can be kept successfully in the aquarium without the anemone and they then seek hiding places in rifts in the coral. The adult fishes form lasting pairs and both partners take part in watching over the eggs which are laid on a stone.

703

Amphiprion sebae [702] is about 8 cm long. It comes from various places in the Pacific and Indian Oceans –for example Batavia, the Isigaki Islands, the Irimote Islands, New Guinea, and elsewhere. It bears a striking resemblance to the species Amphiprion xanthurus which, together with the fish known as Amphiprion chrysurus, is regarded by some as being merely a synonymn for Amphiprion bicinctus. Amphiprion bicinctus [Pl. 55b] has a wide area of distribution – from the Red Sea and the east coast of Africa stretching right across the Indo-Malayan archipelago to southern China and Japan. The fish also lives near several small groups of islands in the Pacific Ocean, especially around coral reefs. The colouring varies with age and size. The young specimens have orange fins and under parts, and instead of the dark, almost black stripes of the adults, there is a series of partly brown and partly orange stripes. This phenomenon may explain the confusion of alternative names already mentioned, Amphiprion xanthurus and Amphiprion chrysurus, which may merely describe the coloration of young specimens of the species Amphiprion bicinctus. This fish grows to a length of about 14 cm (5½ in).

458

Picture 703 shows *Amphiprion frenatus* inside a sea anemone. This fish occurs mainly in the Indian Ocean, around the Philippines and the coasts of the islands of Japan. Its anal fin is either completely light in colouring or becomes darker near the root. The pelvic fins are a smoky black and lighter ot the tips whereas the pectoral fins are pale yellow.

A further species which comes from the coasts of New Guinea and the Philippines is *Amphiprion laticlavius* [704]. It is not likely to be confused with other species: the characteristic second white stripe which extends from the middle of the dorsal fin across the front of the body is a distinctive feature. This stripe looks like an oval mark. The basic colouring is a bright orange-red which, however, may merge into black.

A comparatively rare species in captivity is *Amphiprion perideraion* [705] which inhabits the area between the Sunda archipelago and the Philippines. It is often confused with the smaller species *Amphiprion akallopisos* [707] which is only 7 cm (3 in) long. *Amphiprion perideraion* differs from this species by having a white stripe on the head and the gill covers. The basic colouring of both species is pink. The vertical stripe on the head and the longitudinal stripe down the back are both white. Like other members of the genus *Amphiprion* this fish feeds on small creatures although If necessary it will also take dried foodstuffs. The water temperature

704

in the aquarium should be in the region of 24 to 26°C.

The Wrasses (family **Labridae**) are distinguished by a dorsal fin of which the front spiny part is considerably longer than the rear portion composed of soft rays. The scales are cycloid in form. The

705

459

706

teeth are sharp, often large and prominent, while the lips protrude. They have a set of grinding teeth in the throat on the laryngeal bones. More than 400 species are known, present mainly in tropical waters, although some extend as far north as the coasts of Norway. The majority of them are small and only a few reach a weight of 27 kg (60 lb).

The **Goldsinny,** *Ctenolabrus rupestris* [706], lives in the Mediterranean, the north-west Atlantic, and the Baltic. Its basic colouring is dull orange and there is a dark mark on the upper edge of the tail.

707

This fish grows to a length of 15 cm (6 in) and is sometimes kept in aquaria.

Crenilabrus ocellatus, which builds its nest from seaweed of the genus *Cladophora*, lives in the Adriatic. After spawning it covers the eggs with fronds of seaweed and then carefully protects the nest. *Crenilabrus quinquemaculatus* builds its nest of seaweed of the genus *Cystosira* in the form of a semicircle. In both species in addition to the large males which take on the duty of protecting the nest, there is a number of smaller males who take part in the fertilization of the eggs but then pay no further attention to the nest.

Picture 708 catches *Crenilabrus cinereus* in an unusual position with its head upwards. The basic colouring of this fish is grey-brown, green, or red and the under-belly is yellow. Along the sides there is a brownish stripe and underneath it a series of further parallel stripes which begin underneath the eyes and end in the spot at the root of the tail fin. Its maximum length is 16 cm (6 in).

The **Rainbow Wrasse**, *Coris julis*, is a very brightly coloured fish from the Adriatic and Mediterranean. By day it swims about in a lively fashion but as evening draws on — or if danger threatens — it buries itself in the sand. It is a hermaphrodite. At first it is female but after a short transitional period becomes a male. As a male it grows to a length

708

of 25 cm (10 in) [709]. On the sides of the body the Rainbow Wrasse has an orange longitudinal stripe, while the back is generally bluish-green and the front part of the body has violet stripes. The younger female is brown or olive-brown with one yellow and two dark blue, red, or black stripes on the

709

710

sides. It is interesting that the males which have just undergone the transition from being females are sexually the most active. As soon as they have taken on the beautiful colouring of the male sexual senility sets in. The question therefore remains open whether males during the last stage of their life take any part in reproduction and in the propagation of the species. The two most beautiful species of the genus *Coris* are found in the Indian Ocean around Ceylon *(Coris formosa)* and in the Pacific Ocean in Micronesia and Polynesia *(Coris gaimard)*. In youth they bear little resemblance to the adult specimens. The basic colouring of this species is red to brown with white spots. The adult *Coris formosa* grows to a length of 40 cm (16 in). The basic colouring of its body is grey-blue with black spots, while the throat is a delicate violet, the head yellow to orange with a blue-white band across the eye, while the end of the tail fin is blue, as is the border of the anal fin [Pl. 57]. In the Indo-Pacific region lives *Coris angulata*. Picture 710 shows

this species while it is only 15 cm (6 in) long, while colour plate 56 shows it in the full glory if its adult colouring. Only young specimens can be kept in the aquarium.

The Bird Wrasses of the genus *Gomphosus* are also popular aquarium fishes. *Gomphosus caeruleus* [712] is distributed throughout equatorial zones of the Indo-Pacific region and is found as far west as South Africa. It is difficult to catch since it lives principally in holes in ancient coral reefs. In nature it is up to 30 cm (12 in) long, but in the aquarium it is slightly shorter. A related species, *Gomphosus varius* [711], has the same geographical distribution. This is a lively fish and always seems to be seeking for food with its long beak-like snout. In spite of its small mouth it is able to swallow quite large objects. The colouring is very variable, ranging from olive to red-brown. In the aquarium it requires a water temperature of 24–26°C. Its length is 20–25 cm (8–10 in). It feeds on live food.

55a   *Labeotropheus trewavasae*
55b   *Amphiprion bicinctus*

56 *Coris angulata*

The **Hog Fish** or **Capitaine,** *Lachnolaimus maximus,* which is almost 70 cm (28 in) long, is the only known species of the genus *Lachnolaimus.* It has a wide geographical distribution and has been described under a number of different names. In picture 713 it is accompanied by the **Bluehead,** *Chlorichthys bifasciatus,* in the Caribbean Sea near the coast of Cuba. *Lachnolaimus maximus* is, however, also found around the West Indies and Bermuda. Often it reaches a weight of 5–7 kg (11–15 lb) and is highly valued as a food fish. Its basic colouring is greyish-red or green. Specimens caught at great depths are usually red or orange. The unpaired fins of the adult male are black, as is the forehead; the lower jaw is light yellow. The mouth of the male is larger than that of the female, and the jaw bears strong teeth [714]. The rays of the first dorsal fin are greatly lengthened. The smaller fish in picture 713, the **Bluehead,** *Chlorichthys bifasciatus* (syn. *Thalassoma bifasciatum*), has a deeply indented tail fin. Its body is bi-coloured, the front part being blue with a paler head and the

rear green. It lives in the neighbourhood of the West Indies.

The **Ballan Wrasse,** *Labrus bergylta,* is common in waters around the British Isles. Its distribution extends southwards to the Canary Islands and the Mediterranean. The colouring is variable – green or greenish-brown, often reddish on the back – and changes during growth [715].

Members of the genus *Thalassoma* are popular aquarium fishes living in all the oceans of the world, especially in the warmer areas. All of them are brightly coloured.

The **Moon Wrasse,** *Thalassoma lunare* [716, Pl. 58], has an iridescent green body with a purple-red colouring on the head and fins. The pectoral fins generally have a light blue border while the middle of the tail fin is orange. This species lives in coral reefs. The Moon Wrasse is easy to keep in the aquarium: it is peace-loving, and not fussy about its food. Its length is about 30 cm (12 in). The **Bar-cheeked Wrasse,** *Novaculichthys taeniourus*

[717], occurs in the waters around Zanzibar, Madagascar, Réunion, Mauritius, the East Indies, the Philippines, Melanesia, Micronesia, Polynesia, and the Hawaiian Islands. The body of this little fish is olive-brown with a row of light and dark spots which continue on the fins. Each scale bears a white mark. The dorsal fin is strikingly long and the two first fin rays point forwards like a couple of pennons. The Bar-cheeked Wrasse is about 25 cm (10 in) long. In the aquarium it is aggressive, curious, and will eat large amounts of food. It always seems to be busy building little hiding places for itself by constantly moving pebbles and pieces of coral here and there about the floor of the aquarium: it is able to move whole layers of sand to one side by lying on its side and swishing its tail fin powerfully backwards and forwards. Occasionally it also plucks with its mouth at algae and plants.

The Weevers (family **Trachinidae**) have a long body, compressed at the sides, with two dorsal fins, the second of which, like the anal fin is long.

The mouth is protractile and the second suborbital bone has a projection to which the eye is attached. Members of this family have no swim-bladders and the pelvic fins are immediately under the pectoral fins. The scales are cycloid, and there are poison glands at the bases of the first dorsal fin and of the spines on the gill covers. The **Greater Weever**, *Trachinus draco* [718], which lives in the Atlantic Ocean and the Mediterranean, grows to a length of 40 cm (16 in). The special glands of this fish contain a powerful venom which can even be dangerous to man. The eggs are pelagic. The mouth is comparatively large and set at an angle pointing upwards [719]. This fish lurks in sand, buried up to its eyes, watching for its prey. The flesh of both the above species and of *Trachinus araneus*, which lives in the Adriatic and Mediterranean, is regarded as particularly tasty. The **Lesser Weever**, *Tra-*

718

chinus vipera, is not fished for owing to its small size. The suborder **Blennioidei** is distinguished mainly by having the pelvic fins immediately under the throat. There are at most five fin rays but these may be lacking entirely. The dorsal and anal fins are very long. This suborder contains salt-water fishes. The Blennioidei are divided into nineteen families, typically inhabiting coastal waters of all temperate, tropical, and warm seas.

The **Blenniidae** (Blennies) are generally carnivorous creatures although they will sometimes feed on plant remains. They have a tentacle over the eye. The genus *Blennius* consists of more than forty species, which are found in every ocean in the world except in the tropical parts of the Indian Ocean. Some species live in clumps of seaweed, although the majority are found in coastal waters on the

719

720

721

470

bottom. The males are usually larger than the females. In general these fishes are unsociable and are noted for their voracity.

Blennius pavo [720] which is a native of the Mediterranean, Adriatic and Black seas, is comparatively easy to keep in the aquarium. It hollows out depressions under stones in which individuals live alone. If the aquarium is not large enough or contains too many fishes they become very anti social so that it is not uncommon for the weaker fishes to be beaten down by their stronger fellows. On the other hand, if there Is sufficient space and enough hiding places they maintain their own territories, keeping themselves to themselves and never straying far from the same spot. Their basic colouring is yellow-green with blue-green vertical stripes. Behind the eyes they have a dark oval mark with a light border. The males have a cushion of fat on the head and their body is covered with iridescent blue spots. They grow to a length of about 12 cm (4½ in). They have been successfully bred in aquaria on several occasions.

A related species from the Mediterranean basin is *Blennius sanguinolentus* [721]. This is, likewise, olive-green or occasionally brown or yellow. The colouring changes according to the surface over which the fish is living, but the body is usually covered with irregular, dark, marbled markings. The edges of the pectoral fins are often flecked with red. This species is more robust than the preceding one and grows to a length of 19 cm (7½ in). The **Tompot Blenny**, *Blennius gattorugine* [722], is common in the Mediterranean and Adriatic. Its basic colouring is brown with dark spots and stripes. The vertical stripes run up onto the dorsal fin and there is usually a longitudinal stripe down the side of the body; the under side is reddish-brown. This species grows to a length of 20 cm (8 In). The males have well-developed tentacles near the eyes and on the edge of the dorsal fin there is a black mark. Blennies have tasty flesh.

The Wolf-fishes or Catfishes (family **Anarhichadidae**) include the species *Anarhichas lupus* [723] which is a predator. It has a long body with rudimentary scales, a broad mouth with strong jaws, and conical teeth. The dorsal fin is long and is clearly separated from the tail fin, while the pelvic fins are absent. This fish is up to 2 m (6 ft) long. Its powerful teeth enable it to chew even the hardest-shelled molluscs. It is found in cool seas where it lives close to the bottom, and is fished for in the north Atlantic. It swims very swiftly in eel-like fashion. The Wolf-fish is caught

723

are known. The best-known species is the **Eelpout**
or **Viviparous Blenny**, *Zoarces viviparus*, whose
distribution stretches from the White Sea to the
Bay of Biscay. The eggs are fertilized in the ovary.
The fry develop within the female until they reach
a length of 3–6 cm (1–2½ in). At this point they
are born and resemble the adults completely.
During their development they apparently feed on
secretions in the wall of the ovary. A 20–25 cm
(8–10 in) female bears twenty to forty young, while
larger specimens can give birth to up to 300
offspring. Pictures 724 and 725 show clearly the
great variability in the colouring of these fishes.
The Eelpout grows to a length of about 40 cm (16 in).
Its flesh is tasty and is particularly good when
smoked. *Zoarces anguillaris* which lives along the
coasts of America, is up to 1 m (3 ft) long. Some
members of the related family **Brotulidae** live at
great depths, for example members of the genus
Typhlonus, and have atrophied eyes. One specimen
was caught in the Pacific Ocean at a depth of
4,023 m (13,195 ft) while the genus *Bathynectes*
is found at even greater depths.

both for its excellent flesh and on account of its
thick skin from which handbags are sometimes
made. In some countries the tiny eggs which it
lays on seaweed and algae are eaten.

The Eelpouts (family **Zoarcidae**) have a less
protractile mouth and a scaleless body, or occasionally a few rudimentary scales. The front part of the
dorsal fin is supported by soft fin rays while those
rays at the back of the dorsal fin are spiny. More
than 130 species, arranged in a number of genera,

Members of the suborder **Siganoidei** have two
characteristic spines in the pelvic fins, of which
one is on the outside and the other is on the
inside: in between there are two soft fin rays. The
Rabbitfishes (family **Siganidae**) live in shoals in the
Pacific Ocean. They feed principally on algae. The

724

name Rabbitfishes derives from the way in which they constantly twitch their upper lip. The genus *Siganus* has a deep body, a small mouth, and the anal fin has as many as seven spines. The first spine of the dorsal fin points forward.

The **Reticulated Spinefoot,** *Siganus vermiculatus* [726], a species which comes originally from the Indian Ocean, is kept in the aquarium. It grows to a length of 40 cm (16 in). A related species, the **Blue-spotted Spinefoot,** *Siganus javus,* will feed both on algae and on a variety of animal foodstuff, such as molluscs, shrimps, water fleas, and ghost shrimps.

Members of the suborder **Acanthuroidei** (Surgeonfishes) have a compressed body covered with small ctenoid scales which can sometimes end in small spikes. On each side of the tail there is a sharp curved spine which can be depressed into a socket: this is the 'scalpel' which gives these fishes their name.

726

727

In this suborder there are two families. The first family, **Zanclidae,** was already present in the Lower Eocene, and modern representatives live in the coral reefs of tropical seas. The genus *Zanclus* is found in the Indo-Pacific region. Its members are never longer than 30 cm (12 in) and some species are common and popular inhabitants of sea-water aquaria. The **Moorish Idol,** *Zanclus cornutus* [727], has its distribution stretching from the islands of Zanzibar and Mauritius across the Indian Ocean through the East Indies, Melanesia,

Micronesia, and **Polynesia** up to the coasts of Japan; it is also found in the Gulf of Mexico. The body of this fish is short and deep and the dorsal fin is greatly extended. Its colouring is composed of alternating black and yellow stripes. It is up to 18 cm (7 in) long and shoals with members of its own species in the depths of coral reefs.

The second family, the Surgeonfishes **(Acanthuridae),** also lives in warm seas. On both sides of the tail they have a sharp, moveable spine which can be used as a weapon in fighting with other members of the same species. According to Wickler, Chlupaty, and other authors, these fishes gather in great shoals at evening to spawn. From this shoal individual specimens detach themselves, swim together quickly to the surface, eject their eggs and sperm, and dive down again into the depths. Some species — more than fifty are known — are up to 50 cm (20 in) long and are beautifully coloured. Some species show geographical colour variations, some change colour with age, and others may alter colour according to their mood.

A large number of magnificent species of the genus *Acanthurus* are kept in aquaria. The **White-throated Surgeonfish**, *Acanthurus leucosternon* [728, Pl. 59], is distinguished by its dark blue colouring. It lives in the Indo-Pacific waters and grows to a length of 30 cm (12 in). It has black cheeks, a lemon-yellow or orange dorsal fin, a white anal fin, and a white throat. It prefers plant remains to animal foodstuffs and in the aquarium requires the comparatively high water temperature of 25–28°C. It is a fairly rare fish. The **Lined Surgeonfish**, *Acanthurus lineatus* [Pl. 60a], possesses orange and blue-green longitudinal stripes and a white under-belly. It has the same geographical distribution as the preceding species. In captivity it eats not only algae but also white worms, tubifex worms, mosquito larvae, water fleas, molluscs, shrimps, and lettuce leaves.

Acanthurus wijnbergi [729] is a brightly coloured species which has, however, seldom been imported. This species usually has a brown body with misty patches of purple and fins which are blue-orange and white-striped. The area of the cheeks around the eyes and the mouth is also white. In form it bears a close resemblance to the White-throated Surgeonfish. *Acanthurus dussumieri* is distributed throughout the Pacific Ocean from the southern coasts of Japan to Australia and it is also found in the Philippines, Hawaii, and the waters of South Africa. Its body is brown-red with fine, wavy, blue stripes. There is a yellow to golden-orange stripe crossing the eyes. The dorsal fin and the root of the tail fin are likewise orange, while the throat and under-belly are blue. The tail fin is also blue and decorated with black spots. There is a blue longitudinal stripe running the length of the body close under the dorsal fin. This species is not very suitable for keeping in aquaria owing to its length — up to 50 cm (20 in) — although it is very attractively coloured. Picture 730 shows *Acanthurus dussumieri* accompanied by two cleaner fishes, *Labroides dimidiatus.*

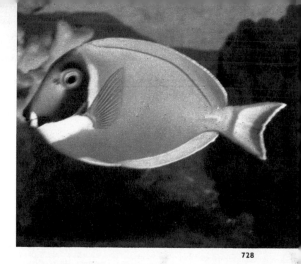

728

729

730

731

732

733

476

The **Five–banded Surgeonfish**, *Acanthurus triostegus*, [731], is somewhat smaller and is distributed throughout the Indian and Pacific oceans; it has a maximum length of 22 cm (8½ in). It occurs around Mauritius, Réunion, the Seychelles, and in an area which stretches from the Cocos Islands to Hawaii. Its colouring is not particularly striking, the basic shade being silver, olive-grey or light brown. The vertical stripes on the sides are dark purple to black. During the spawning season the males become darker and often have a black back. This fish usually lives in shoals on flat reefs, where it browses on algae. In picture 732 it is seen accompanied by the inevitable cleaner fish.

The **Flag-tail Surgeonfish**, *Paracanthurus hepatus* [Pl. 60b], is very brightly coloured. It is present mainly in the Indo-Pacific region, especially off the coasts of Ceylon. Its colouring is very intense: sky-blue and lemon-yellow with a black pattern. It is up to 25 cm (10 in) long. The correct water temperature for this fish is between 25–30°C. In addition to algae it feeds on *Mysis*, molluscs, tubifex worms, and white worms.

The genus *Naso* contains many popular fishes for seawater aquaria. This genus has a pair of fixed spines in place of the projecting blades on each side of the tail. Occasionally these take the form of bony knobs. Some species also have a knob on the forehead or in some cases a long horn. They are up to 60 cm (24 in) long. The **Brown Unicorn-fish**, *Naso* brevirostris [733], is distributed throughout the Pacific Ocean, especially around Bikini Atoll, the Hawaiian Islands, and Okinawa. It has dark brown flanks with a lighter under-belly. The dorsal and anal fins are dark brown, while the fin rays and the pectoral fins are brown with white membranes, and the abdominal fins are light brown.

The **Short-horned Unicornfish**, *Naso annulatus* [734], is light or dark greyish-brown on the flanks. The dorsal fin is pale where it meets the body, but almost black in the middle and has a white border. Often there is a white ring around the spine of the tail running down to the root of the anal fin.

The beautifully coloured *Naso lituratus* [735] is particularly popular among aquarists. This is present in large numbers around the coral reefs of the Pacific Ocean. The body is violet, dark brown, or dark purple, while the lips and the stripes which lead from the eyes down to the mouth, the forehead and the anal fin are orange. The dorsal fin is light blue or purple at the root. The pelvic fins are light brown while the pectoral fins often have a whitish rim. For this species, as for the others of this genus, a temperature of 24–26°C is recommended. In addition to vegetable food such as algae and even boiled spinach, *Naso lituratus* will feed on animal matter such as tubifex worms, ox heart, and *Mysis*, although not all specimens take to animal foods with equal readiness. This fish must be handled with great care.

The **Blue Surgeonfish**, *Zebrasoma xanthurus* [736], has an arresting appearance. Its whole body is dark blue while the

734

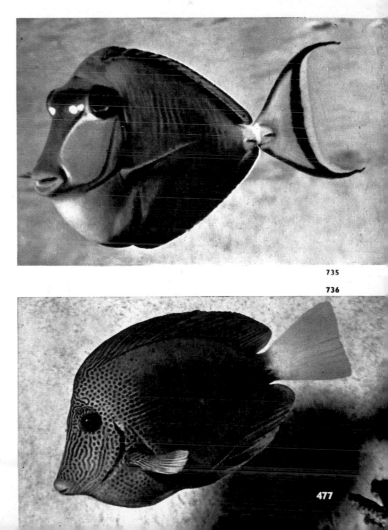

735

736

737

738

and the pectoral and tail fins are covered with light spots. The anal and dorsal fins are stretched to make a vivid display. The narrow bands on both these fins often go right across the body. The fish grows to an overall length of 30 cm (12 in).

The fishes of the suborder **Scombroidei** (Mackerels and Bonitos) possess two dorsal fins of which the second continues as a series of little fins. The pectoral fins are set very high up each side of the body. The body is covered with small, cycloid scales, but in some species scales are entirely absent. In this suborder there are two superfamilies divided into seven families, of which four are recent and three are extinct. The group has great economic significance both as food fishes and as sport. They are typically fishes of the upper layers of the open sea.

head is lighter and covered with small red to black spots. The lips and the tips of the pectoral fins are yellow to orange in colouring. Once accustomed to the aquarium it develops a vast appetite. It prefers live food – for example shrimps and *Mysis*.

The **Sail-finned Surgeonfish,** *Zebrasoma velife-rum* [737], has characteristic high anal and dorsal fins. This species comes from the Red Sea and has a very attractive pattern. The body colouring is olive-green with vertical orange stripes which change to a row of dots near the belly. The head

The family of Mackerels **(Scombridae)** existed as early as the Eocene. Today about fifty species are known. They have no swim-bladder. The **Common Mackerel,** *Scomber scombrus* [738], lives pelagically in shoals in the north Atlantic, the White Sea, and the Black Sea, and along the coasts of America from Cape Hatteras to Labrador. It grows to a length of 50 cm (20 in) and weighs 450 gm ($\frac{1}{2}$ lb). This fish does not undertake great migrations, and feeds on crustaceans. Spawning takes place during May

739

740

741

and after spawning the Mackerel swim northwards. However, winter brings them south again, but far from the coasts. The eggs are pelagic. In the Soviet part of the Black Sea the annual catch amounts to between 400,000 and 430,000 tons, and that from the north-east Atlantic to over 1,000,000 tons. Only 3,900 tons of Mackerel were landed at British ports in 1968.

The Sailfishes of the family **Istiophoridae** have a strikingly high dorsal fin which is some species is divided into two parts. The body is covered with small scales. In the tropical parts of the Pacific, the Atlantic, and the Indian oceans, three genera of this fish are known, all of which have economic significance. The genus *Istiophorus* [740] has a continuous dorsal fin divided into two parts.

The Swordfishes, family **Xiphiidae**, whose members are scaleless and entirely lack pelvic fins, are related to the Sailfishes. The teeth are absent in adult specimens. The genus *Xiphias*, has only one species *gladius* [739], the **Swordfish**, which is widespread. The Swordfish grows to a length of 5–6 m (16–19 ft), and attains a weight of some 300 kg (660 lb). It lives near the surface in warm seas; the eggs, too, are pelagic. The fry have long jaws in which the teeth are still present and there is a series of spines on the gill covers. Swordfishes undertake migrations over great distances and follow shoals of the fishes on which they feed. They are only of any great economic importance in Japan although local fisheries exist elsewhere. In the USA, trolling for Swordfishes is a great sport. From time to time they have been known to attack ships without any apparent reason: pieces of the 'sword' stuck into lumps of timber can be seen in various maritime museums. The Swordfish is a nuisance to fishermen since the shoals of Tuna which they hope to catch tend to give it a wide berth. Swordfishes are swift and powerful swimmers.

The suborder **Anabantoidei** (Labyrinth-fishes) shows strong similarities to the Perches. It is distinguished from them by the much folded and highly vascular organs in the upper side of each gill chamber, known as the labyrinth, forming an

742

auxiliary breathing apparatus which enables the fishes to take in oxygen from the air. This breathing organ consists anatomically of a modification of the first gill arch. In its tubes there is a number of lamellae which are covered with a membrane containing numerous, greatly enlarged, superficial blood vessels. Thus the blood is enriched with oxygen taken in through the capillaries in contact with the air. Both the dorsal and anal fins are equipped with spines. The scales are ctenoid. In this suborder there is only one family, the **Anabantidae,** which is subdivided by some authors. It is found in southern Asia and in the tropical parts of Africa. The Anabantidae may have evolved from a common ancestor of the **Percoidei** and may owe the evolution of their breathing organs to the changed habitat in which they found themselves – shallow, muddy, often stagnant, tropical waters, with a poor oxygen content in which the intake of oxygen through the gills was insufficient to support life. During the spawning season some species build bubble nests on the surface of the

water in which they lay their eggs. A number of species have been kept in aquaria.

In the Indo-Malayan archipelago and in Thailand there is a number of Fighting Fishes of the genus *Betta.* One of the most popular aquarium fishes is the 6 cm (2½ in) long **Siamese Fighting Fish,** *Betta splendens.* Specimens from Thailand and Vietnam are usually green, while those from Singapore are red. Through careful breeding a long-finned form has been developed. In picture 741 green and red males can be seen together: both have well-developed fins. The male builds a bubble nest which has an area of about 10 sq cm (4 sq in) and is constructed out of a secretion from a membrane in the mouth. Spawning takes place underneath this nest. Afterwards the male beds down the eggs in the nest and protects them from the female which is usually removed from the tank after spawning. The fry emerge as soon as twenty-four to thirty-six hours after fertilization at a temperature of 27–30°C. They are protected by the male

743

57　Coris formosa

58 Moon Wrasse *(Thalassoma lunare)*

until they are able to swim independently. In their homeland Fighting Fishes are matched against each other in competitions resembling cock fights or prize fights. In addition to the original green form a large number of colour variations has been bred in the course of several decades, and forms are known with an astonishing brilliance of shades ranging from light green, blue, red and yellow to olive, dark blue and black. Colour plate 61a shows a yellow Fighting Fish with red fins which was achieved by crossing a red form with a yellow one after painstaking selective breeding.

The **Thick-lipped Gourami,** *Colisa labiosa* [742], is a member of the genus *Colisa* coming from southern Burma. The male is 8 cm (3 in) long — slightly larger than the female. The iridescent spots on both sides of the body are grey-green, and the thread-like abdominal fins of the male are red while those of the female are colourless. The borders of the tail fin are red in the female and blue in the male. The eggs are laid in a bubble nest on the water's surface and owing to their large oil content they are lighter than water. This fish has been kept in Europe since 1904.

The **Giant Gourami,** *Colisa fasciata* [Pl. 61b], is very similar to the Thick-lipped Gourami. This fish is an inhabitant of muddy waters in India and Burma. If it is kept in an aquarium it requires a temperature of between 24 and 28°C which

should be raised to 30° C for breeding. However, adult members of this species will survive temperature drops as low as 15°C. This fish is omnivorous.

The **Dwarf Gourami,** *Colisa lalia* [743], which comes from India, is a small deep-bodied fish. Its basic colouring is blue with diagonal red stripes. It is comparatively shy in the aquarium. The bubble nest is built between leaves or other parts of plants floating on the water's surface. For spawning a temperature of 30°C is recommended. The smallest species of the genus is the **Honey Gourami,** *Colisa chuna*, which is only 4–4.5 cm (1½ in) long. This fish occurs in north-east India, Assam, the Ganges, the Brahmaputra, and the Hooghly rivers. Various different colour forms are known. They are very easy to keep in the aquarium and will spawn at a temperature as low as 24°C. However, they have only 150–250 young at a time and when the fry are very small they must be fed with rotifers for one or two weeks: they are unable to catch *Cyclops* nauplii which spring away too fast. Both the young and the females have a brown band along the sides by which they may be easily distinguished from the males. Colour plate 62 shows the general coloration.

The **Paradisefish,** *Macropodus opercularis*, lives in the waters of Korea, China, South Vietnam, and Taiwan. The male [744] is 9 cm (3½ in) long. The body is comparatively long and the vertical fins

744

745

are greatly extended. The basic colouring of this attractive, lively, little fish is brown, green, or grey. Blue-green and crimson stripes alternate along the sides of the body. A temperature of 15–20°C is adequate for the adults and 20–24°C suffices for breeding: if the temperature is raised spawning is very successful. This fish is not suitable for mixed aquaria since it is very pugnacious. Hungry specimens are used to destroy planarian worms which are otherwise very difficult to remove from the tank.

Typical Gourami country is the flooded paddy fields and ponds of Kuang-Chou in Canton which is shown in picture 745. Like other Gouramis, the Paradisefish usually attaches itself to floating plants. And the irrigation canals and water courses of the rice fields offer just this habitat, with their excellent growths of water hyacinths (Eichhornia crassipes). In picture 746 such a plant can be seen floating in an irrigation channel in the province of Canton in China. The Paradisefish was one of the earliest of aquarium fishes. It was first brought to France in

746

the year 1869 from Ningpo by the French consul Simon; the Parisian ichthyologist P. Carbonier bred it successfully in captivity; the fish was known in Germany by 1876 and quickly became widespread and popular. The theory that the familiar long-finned form of the Paradisefish was the result of artificial breeding by Chinese fish fanciers was exploded by Kreyenberg. For a period before spawning the adults should have a rich, live diet.

The bubble nest is built by the male [747] and this often takes several hours or even days depending on how close to being ready for spawning the partners are. While building the nest the male chases away the female but later he lures her towards it. If the female is ready to eject her eggs both fishes place themselves head to head, swimming around each other and turning quickly upwards until they are situated side by side. Then the male embraces the female with his body [748], both fishes turn their bellies upwards, eject their eggs or sperm and gradually sink down to the bottom together [749]. The male recovers somewhat more quickly than the female and begins immediately to collect the eggs and carry them up to the nest on the water's surface. Spawning is repeated at various intervals until the female has laid all her eggs.

A pure albino mutation with the typical red eyes has been bred from the original Paradisefishes. In 1935 Ahl described the **Black Paradisefish** *Macropodus opercularis concolor*, the male of which can be seen in picture 750. This subspecies has

750

a rather less striking dark colouring. The vertical stripes on the sides of the body are absent, and during the spawning season the body becomes an intense black. However, little is known about the origin of this fish. Dr. Ladiges is of the opinion that this may be a closely related subspecies of the original Paradisefish, *Macropodus opercularis*. This view was based on the assumption that the Paradisefish is indeed the result of selective breeding by Chinese fish fanciers. The Black Paradisefish has similar breeding habits to the Paradisefish.

The **Gourami**, *Osphronemus goramy* [751], which is up to 60 cm (24 in) long, is an inhabitant of the East Indies. In its native land it is regarded principally as a food fish. Only young specimens are suitable for the aquarium. The body of the fishes is oval and compressed at the sides. It has black flecks, especially on the head, while the back is dark grey and the under parts are yellowish. The fish are grey or reddish-grey. Mature specimens can, according to Rachow, be entirely red. The young are a light reddish-brown and have several dark vertical bands and a light ringed spot above the rear part of the anal fin. In older specimens the forehead is

greatly swollen and forms a fatty protuberance [752]. The dorsal and anal fins of the male are pointed at the ends. These fishes are quite hardy and can stand low temperatures. With proper feeding and addition of plant foodstuff, such as oats, they grow quickly. In the second year of their life they are already 20–30 cm (8–12 in) long and are rewarding exhibits for a large public aquarium. The male attends to the spawn and fry in a bubble nest. An interesting species is the so-called **Kissing Gourami**, *Helostoma temincki* [753]. It lives in the waters of the Malayan Peninsula and Indonesia and is up to 30 cm (12 in) long. In captivity, however, it does not reach this length. This Gourami has a striking coloration with its dark, olive-green back and almost white belly. The sexes are difficult to distinguish. The fish is omnivorous and requires a plentiful supply of plant matter. The name Kissing Gourami derives from the fact that these fishes have a habit of pressing their thick-lipped mouths together as if they are kissing. In fact, however, these appear to be quarrels between rivals. Little is known about the reproductive biology of these fishes in the aquarium. In its native land it is valued as a food fish.

One of the most attractive Gouramis is without doubt the **Pearl** or **Mosaic Gourami,** *Trichogaster leeri*. In picture 754 a male is following a female along the bed of the aquarium. This Gourami is 11 cm (4½ in) long and comes from the waters of the Malayan Peninsula, Thailand, Sumatra, and Borneo. On a yellowish-brown basic colouring there is a number of tiny white and yellow flecks with a mother-of-pearl iridescence. The pectoral fins and the front part of the anal fin are orange coloured or red to violet. The male is larger and darker in colouring than the female. It is a friendly though rather shy little fish and loves warmth. During the spawning season it builds a huge bubble nest on the water's surface and the male pushes the female up to it from the bottom.

The **Three-spot Gourami,** *Trichogaster trichopterus*, is a native of the Malayan Peninsula, Thailand, South Vietnam, and Indonesia. It grows to a length of 15 cm (6 in) and in body form resembles *Trichogaster leeri*. Its colouring varies greatly. The basic colour is a silvery olive-green or blue. On its sides

it has two very noticeable flecks which grow intense if the fish is excited; one is immediately under the dorsal fin and the second at the root of the tail. The fins are green or grey with a number of white, yellow or orange dots. They are mature once they reach a length of 7–8 cm (2½–3 in). Before spawning the female is chased by the male, as in other species. At this time the colouring of the fish changes and the whole body is marbled in black and grey and the more excited the fish becomes the darker the colouring. In picture 755 the male is embracing the female underneath the nest. Spawning takes place in the same way as in *Trichogaster leeri*. After spawning it is a good idea to remove the female to another tank so that she does not disturb the male as he cares for the offspring. The male places a further layer of bubbles on the nest and will not allow the female near it under any circumstances. The young emerge after about three days and there are usually up to 1,000 fry from one spawning: these must be fed at first on live plankton, preferably rotifers. The 'labyrinth' begins to develop in the third or fourth week.

753

754

A subspecies, the **Blue Gourami,** *Trichogaster trichopterus sumatranus* [756], which is nearly 30 cm (12 in) long, occurs in Sumatra. The basic colouring is blue. It is kept in exactly the same way as the typical form although it is somewhat more warmth-loving. In 1960 a colour mutation was brought to Europe from the USA under the commercial name *Trichogaster trichopterus cosby* [757]. The designation

755

'cosby', or sometimes incorrectly 'crosby', is actually the name of the lucky breeder who discovered this mutation among his fishes and was able to breed it independently as a pure form. American aquarists use the generally acceptable term '**Opaline Gourami**'.

The **Talking** or **Croaking Gourami**, *Trichopsis vittatus* [758], which grows to a length of 6.5 cm (2½ in), lives in South-East Asia and Indonesia. The fish is yellow-green to brown with a white area on its belly, the sides of the body have a bluish-white sheen with light stripes and there are three or four dark brown longitudinal bands. The eye is red on the outside with an inner pupil of green. The male has a longer anal and dorsal fin than the female. Spawning, which may be difficult to induce, is most successful in spring at a water temperature of 28–30°C in a tank placed in a sunny spot and provided with a thick growth of water plants. The males emit a croaking sound which apparently originates in the labyrinth.

A related species, the **Dwarf Croaking Gourami,** *Trichopsis pumilus* [Pl. 64a], is smaller – only about 3.5 cm (1½ in) long – and brighter in colour. It comes from South Vietnam, Thailand, and Sumatra. The fish builds its nest from tiny bubbles of foam on the underside of the leaf of a water plant or in a thicket of fine-leafed plants, or even in a flowerpot lying on its side. Often the eggs are laid without a nest, directly on the underside of a leaf of some large-leafed water plant growing near the bottom. The number of eggs is small and amounts only to a few dozen. The fry emerge after about thirty-six hours at a water temperature of 27–28°C. This species too emits a croaking sound – or at any rate the males do – although it is somewhat quieter than *Trichopsis vittatus*.

The genus *Ctenopoma* contains the African Climbing Perches. Their dorsal fin is longer than the anal fin and the mouth comparatively large, while the gill covers have teeth around the edges. The labyrinth is not well developed.

The **Silver-bellied Climbing Perch,** *Ctenopoma argentoventer* [759], comes from the tropical waters of West Africa, especially the area of the Niger. It has an interrupted lateral line organ and the scales are comparatively large. This fish is 15 cm (6 in) long. It is a pugnacious species and therefore not suitable for mixed aquaria. It has a healthy appetite and will swallow both small fishes and large pieces of plant matter. It requires a high temperature and spawns at 28–30°C. The eggs, which are laid in the open water, float to the surface owing to their high oil content.

760

The suborder **Luciocephaloidei** is often treated as a family in the suborder Anabantoidei. However, the labyrinth in this suborder has a simpler structure in that the multitudinous inner lamellae are not present, nor is there a swim-bladder. The mouth is protrusible and the pelvic fins are attached directly to the shoulder part of the body. The family **Luciocephalidae** is represented by a single species, the **Pike-head**, *Luciocephalus pulcher* [760]. It lives in Malaya, Sumatra, and Borneo and grows to a length of 15–18 cm (6–7 in). Its basic colouring is yellow and it has dark brown longitudinal bands and stripes. It is a predator and lurks for its prey among the plants near the water's surface. It is a difficult fish to keep in aquaria and so far has not been successfully bred. The theory that this fish is live-bearing has so far not been substantiated. It manages to swallow five or six female Guppies each day. No further information is available about its biology in the natural state.

Members of the suborder **Gobioidei** have between one and eight flexible, unbranched rays in the first dorsal fin. The pelvic fins are often fused together forming a single fin: they are situated directly under the pectoral fins. In most species there is no swim-bladder. Approximately 600 species are known, mostly small fishes of the sea coasts, particularly common in the tropics. In the opinion of some authors, fossils found in the Lower Tertiary can be attributed to this suborder. A number of species have adapted to fresh-water life.

The **Eleotridae** (Sleepers) have a pair of distinct pelvic fins. The pupil of the eye is opaque giving the impression that the fish is blind. In this family there are more than 100 species divided into several genera.

The **Australian** or **Purple-striped Gudgeon** or **Sleepy Trout**, *Mogurnda mogurnda* [761], lives in the rivers and along the coasts of central, northern, and eastern Australia, and is also found in New Guinea. It is 17 cm (6½ in) long and has a cylindrical body with highly variable colouring. The basic colouring is olive-brown while the sides are covered with enormous dark spots which sometimes join together to form longitudinal stripes. On the gill-cover there is a brown mark with a white border. The fins are dark with red spots and a light coloured edge. During the spawning season the colouring becomes more intensive. The female is larger than the male. These fishes are omnivorous and spawn at a temperature of 25–28°C.

761

It is generally a good idea to keep several females with a single male. The eggs are laid in strings of between 150 and 300 and are attached by a fine thread to stones. The male undertakes the care of the spawn. The fry feed from the outset on live foodstuff and in captivity these fishes reproduce very easily. The less strikingly coloured *Perccottus glehni* [762] lives in the Amur river. It grows to a length of up to 25 cm (10 in) and is only rarely kept in aquaria. The eastern coast of Mexico, the southern states of the USA, and the West Indies are the home of the **Spotted** or **Striped Sleeper Goby**, *Dormitator maculatus* [763], which in nature grows to a length of 30 cm (24 in). From time to time this species is imported to Europe but has so far achieved little popularity among European aquarists. It is a predator and in the aquarium will attack smaller species of fish. Its eggs are small and are laid in rows on stones. The females have remarkably fat bellies. The fry emerge after only twenty to twenty-six hours at a temperature of 25°C and grow quickly, being best suited by brackish water.

764

The **Gobiidae** (Gobies) are characterized by pelvic fins which in some species are distinct but in most are fused together, although all of them form a weak sucking organ which helps the fish to maintain its position on a surface. Most species live in coastal waters of warm seas and occasionally also in estuarine brackish water. Sometimes they even move upstream into fresh water.

The most common species to be kept in aquaria is the **Golden-banded Goby** or **Bumblebee Fish**, *Brachygobius xanthozona* [764], which is about 4.5 cm (2 in) long. It lives in rivers, particularly in the estuaries of Sumatra, Borneo, and Java and is commonly confused with *Brachygobius nunus* which comes from the Malay Peninsula and Thailand. The markings are very variable, especially so far as the form of the alternating brown and light orange vertical stripes is concerned. The basic colouring is dark brown to black and the lighter bands often form irregular markings. Specimens coming from

some areas, however, are completely black. Brackish water is recommended for keeping in aquaria, (one or two tablespoonfuls of sea salt to every ten litres of water), since in fresh water these fishes are very susceptible to disease. The most suitable temperature is between 24 and 30°C. The female lays about 100–150 eggs on a stone or in a flowerpot. The fry hatch within four to five days or, depending on the water temperature, even earlier. The adults live near the bottom and feed on small creatures of every kind. The Bumblebee Fish is not suitable for keeping in mixed aquaria.

The Mudskippers (family **Periophthalmidae**) are sometimes regarded as a subfamily of the Gobiidae and possess some very interesting features. The eye, equipped with an upper lid and, rather like the eye of a frog, is situated on the top of the head and can be moved in any direction. The upper jaw projects beyond the lower jaw. The pectoral fins are equipped with powerful muscles which enable

765

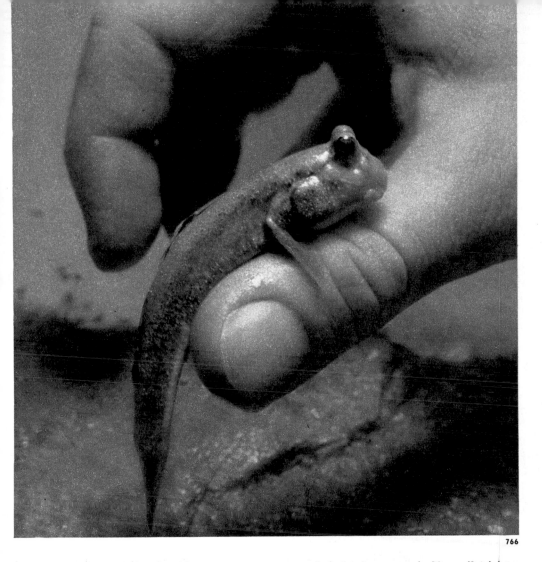

766

the fish to move on land. Two dorsal fins are present and the front one has undivided fin rays. The tail fin has a broad flattened lower edge. All the Mudskippers are small, ranging from 15 to 30 cm (6 to 12 in) in length. They live in large numbers in marshy coasts in the tropical regions of the Indian and Atlantic oceans and in river estuaries in the inter-tidal zone. Brackish water is necessary if they are to be kept in the aquarium. They move along the bank by means of their pectoral, pelvic, and tail fins in a series of sudden leaps. There are several genera of Mudskippers. Members of the genus *Periophthalmus* are only 20 cm (8 in) long. *Periophthalmus barbarus* [765] has an uncommonly wide distribution: from the Red Sea and East Africa through Madagascar, southern Asia, and Indonesia to Australia. This species is 15 cm (6 in) long. The first rays of the dorsal fin are remarkably long. These creatures are sometimes found climbing up the roots and trunks of mangroves. They can stay a surprisingly long time out of the water since the gill-covers are able to seal the gills completely, preventing them from drying out. *Periophthalmus koelreuteri* [766] lives in South-East Asia.

The arrangement of the eyes on top of the head and their incredible mobility can be seen clearly in picture [767]. These creatures feed on a wide variety of live foods. In the aquarium they can be fed on insects, worms, beetles, and flies. Secondary sexual differences have not been fully studied. They have not yet been successfully bred in captivity.

The most primitive members of the suborder **Cottoidei** show some connections with the Percoidei. The evolution which has adapted the Cottoidei to a life on the sea bed can be observed in the degeneration of the swim-bladder and in a large bony covering on the head. In some species there are spines on the head equipped with poison glands, whose venom can often be dangerous to man. They are all fishes which move very little and have large heads and broad mouths. The pectoral fins are not used for movement but to circulate the water around the fish as it lies motionless on the sea bed. Apparently the Percoidei were originally inhabitants of warmer seas but they are now found in fresh water and in the Arctic and Antarctic.

The most note-worthy sea dwellers among the Cottoidei are the **Tetrarogidae** — small fishes anything from 2.5–23 cm (1-9 in) long with spiny fins. These creatures generally live in hiding places on the sea bottom and have poison glands on their spines. Picture [768] shows the 13 cm (5 in) long *Amblyapistus binotatus* from the Indian Ocean.

767

768

498

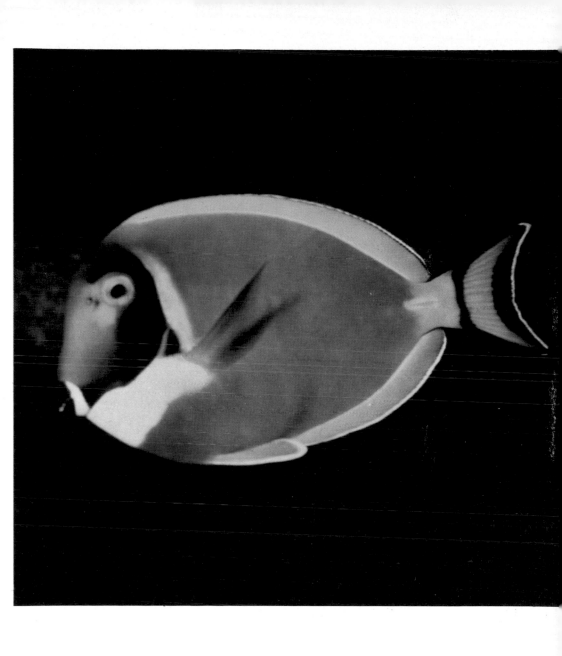

59　White-throated Surgeonfish (*Acanthurus leucosternon*)

60a Lined Surgeonfish *(Acanthurus lineatus)*
60b Flag-tail Surgeonfish *(Paracanthurus hepatus)*

Taenianotus triacanthus has occasionally been imported from the Hawaiian Islands and grows to a length of 8 cm (3 in). It is also found in various places on the coasts of South Africa and in the Indian Ocean. It has a scaleless body and sheds its skin fairly frequently — at times as often as every fourteen days — in much the same way as snakes do.

The **Scorpion-fishes** (family **Scorpaenidae**), which are known from as early as the Paleocene, are close relatives. of the Tetrarogidae. The species of the genus *Scorpaena* live hidden among stones or buried in sand. They move along by using their powerful, broad, pectoral fins. These creatures feed on small fishes. *Scorpaena scrofa* and *Scorpaena porcus* live in the Mediterranean and Black seas. The secretion of the poison glands at the base of the fin rays can be extremely painful. However, the fishes are very tasty. They are about 40 cm (16 in) long. Of those species which are found in the tropics the Firefishes of the genus *Pterois* are particularly brightly coloured; they are very popular in

sea-water aquaria. One species which is particularly popular among aquarists is the **Red Firefish,** *Pterois volitans* [769]. It lives in the Red Sea, the

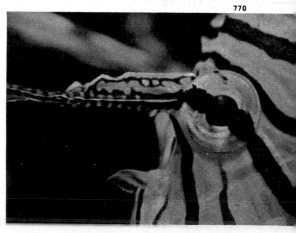

771

coastal waters of South Africa, and Polynesia. There are alternating dark and light bands on its body. The long dorsal and pectoral fins take on bizarre shapes. These fishes are 15–30 cm (6–12 in) in length. Picture 770 shows the fringe above the eyes which in this species is particularly well

developed. The Red Firefish survives well in the aquarium.

In *Pterois antennata* [771] the fringe above the eyes is small and the front rays of the pectoral fins are turned upwards.

Pterois lunulatus [772], which has a similar geographical distribution to the species already described, has, likewise, only small fringes above the eyes. The fin rays are slightly shorter and the body is coloured pink with dark vertical stripes. There is usually a number of dark flecks on the pectoral fins.

774

Pterois radiata is distinguished by simple fin rays with almost no membrane between them. Picture 773 shows a young specimen while picture 774 shows an adult. The poison of some species of *Pterois* is similar to cobra venom and the serum used as an antidote for a cobra bite is also effective against the poison of these fishes. They are voracious creatures which can be quickly tamed; they can be fed on dead meat in the aquarium.

Pterois miles [775] has broad dark stripes on its body and the membrane between the rays of the pectoral and dorsal fins is well formed. The pectoral fins form a sort of fan. The basic colouring is brownish-pink and the dark bands have a white border.

Some smaller but similar species, such as the **Zebra Firefish** [776] belong to the genus *Dendrochirus*: these live in the Indo-Pacific region and are about 15 cm (6 in) long.

The Stonefishes of the genus *Synanceja* which are sometimes elevated into an independent family **Synanciidae** are closely related to *Pterois*. The most familiar species, coming from the tropical part of the Indo-Pacific region, are *Synanceja horrida* and *Synanceja verrucosa*. The body is scaleless and covered with soft, thread-like, elastic warts. These hideous and repellent creatures sometimes look like small seaweed covered stones. The needle-sharp spines of the dorsal fin have a small groove containing poison glands. If one treads on this creature the spines penetrate the sole of the foot and the poison is injected under pressure into the muscles: if one of the larger arteries or veins is penetrated the poison quickly spreads throughout the whole body. The victim may die in agony after a few hours. No antidote for this poison is known. Apparently washing the wound with boiling water is supposed to help. Even if the victim survives the wound, amputation

775

of the foot is often unavoidable owing to secondary infection.

There are about twenty species of the related larger fishes of the genus *Sebastes*. These are found principally in the north Atlantic. The **Norway Haddock** or **Redfish**, *Sebastes viviparus* [777], bears live young. The fry have been mainly observed around the Lofoten Islands, Iceland, and Newfoundland. They are inhabitants of coastal waters. *Sebastes norvegicus* grows to a length of up to 90 cm (36 in) and a weight of 10 kg (22 lb). It has

a deep body covered with scales and is a fish of moderately deep waters in the north Atlantic living on the coasts of Norway, Greenland, and Iceland. This fish has in recent years assumed an increasingly important role as a food fish and is usually marketed in prepacked frozen portions.

The family **Triglidae** (Gurnards) is known from the Upper Eocene. The front part of the head of these fishes is almost completely covered by the greatly enlarged first bones of the suborbital arch. The anal fin has no spines. The first two or three fin rays on

776

the underside of the pectoral fin are not connected with the fin itself: they serve rather to sample the bottom when the fish is feeding and apparently function as organs of touch. Gurnards are not generally longer than 70 cm (28 in) and their bodies are covered with scales or bony plates. In the Adriatic there are some eight species of which the largest, the **Tub Gurnard** or **Saphirine Gurnard,** *Trigla lucerna* [778], is up to 70 cm (28 in) long. When it is on the bottom it stretches out its three independent pectoral fin rays [779]. The colouring is uninteresting but fairly variable from

brown to orange and from green to grey. The belly is white or off-white and the pectoral fins are as a rule dark green to dark purple. These fishes have little economic significance and are occasionally kept in public aquaria.

The Bullheads or Sculpins (family **Cottidae**) are characteristically scaleless and spindle-shaped, with a large, flat-topped head. The body is sometimes covered with bony plates and spines. The pelvic fins have one hard and between two and five soft fin rays. The second dorsal fin has the same

777

form as the anal fin. There are more than 200 species of Sculpins, mostly living in the sea, arranged in some dozen genera — fresh-water Sculpins are fewer in number and are found principally in North America and Asia with only one or two in Europe. Their occurrence in fresh water is a result of secondary migration which apparently took place either in the Tertiary or later between the Ice Ages.

The **Miller's-Thumb** or **Bullhead,** *Cottus gobio* [780], is 10–15 cm (4–6 in) long and is common throughout Europe with the exception of the Pyrenees, Italy, and the Caucasus. Its distribution stretches eastwards as far as the Urals. It lives between or beneath stones and feeds on the fauna of the river bed and on gammarids. In the spring, which is its breeding season, it lays orange-coloured eggs in holes under stones where they are protected by the male. The Bullhead is an important item in the food chain of predators, particularly Trout, in the upper waters of rivers.

The **Bull Rout,** *Myoxocephalus scorpius* [781], is a veritable giant among the European sea-water Cottidae. Its distribution stretches from the Bay of Biscay to the far north and from Greenland along the American coast to Cape Hatteras. A whole series of geographical forms have been described in the literature of the subject. The larger specimens from the Arctic Ocean grow to a length of about 1 m (3 ft). Southwards the Bull Routs become smaller. In the North Sea they are at most 50 cm (20 in) in length and in the Baltic less than 30 cm (12 in). During winter they live in deeper regions, while in summer they move to stony shallows. The large American and Asian species live in northern seas.

The Lumpsuckers, family **Cyclopteridae,** are closely related to the Cottidae. They differ from them mainly through the sucking organ on the belly which is formed from a growing together of the pelvic fins with an outer rim of skin. The skin is very thick and has no scales, although it may be covered with lumps. The first dorsal fin is very short in the young but entirely absent in adults. This slow-moving fish descends to remarkable depths. There are more than fifty species divided into several genera.

The **Lumpsucker, Sea Hen, Hen-Fish,** or **Lump,** *Cyclopterus lumpus* [782], grows to a length of approximately 1 m (3 ft). It lives on rocky coasts of Europe. Between 80,000 and 136,000 eggs are laid in the inter-tidal and sublittoral zones so that

during the ebb tide they often lie exposed to the air. The male protects the eggs and since he will not leave them even when the water has receded, he is an easy prey for land mammals and birds. However, even in the sea these fishes are easily caught by Sharks, Whales, Dolphins and other predators. The male is smaller than the female and during the spawning season his body has a marbled pattern. The female has a deep, blue-black colouring while the young are a dirty greenish-brown like that of the seaweed among which they live.

The **Dactylopteriformes**, (Flying Gurnards) possess several protruding bones set with thorns on their heads. The first unusually long vertebra is in fact an amalgam of the first three vertebrae. The pectoral fins are paired and are very long. The whole body is covered with coarse scales. The family **Dactylopteridae** is sometimes called **Cephala-canthidae.** Members of the genus *Dactylopterus* have a square head protected by strong bones. There are two dorsal fins and the swim-bladder is divided length-ways into two chambers. This genus lives principally in warm seas and its best-known member is the **Flying Gurnard,** *Dactylopterus volitans* [783], which is present in the Mediterranean and on the southern European, African, and American coasts of the Atlantic Ocean. It is able to 'fly' through the water, but the main function of the brightly coloured pectoral fins is to distract

its enemies. This fish grows to a length of about 50 cm (20 in).

The order **Thunniformes** (Tunnies) consists of sea-water fishes, usually of considerable length. The Thunniformes are closely related to the Scombroidei: they have two dorsal fins and one anal fin and the second dorsal fin and the anal fin are divided into a number of smaller fins. These creatures are known from as early as the Lower Eocene. At the present day they are of great economic significance and according to Nikolski 350,000 tons of them are caught each year of which only 30,000 tons come from the Atlantic, the rest being caught in the Pacific.

The family **Thunnidae** possess a keel on either side of the tail, and the body is covered with scales. The **Tuna**, *Thunnus thynnus* [784], lives in the Atlantic Ocean and in the Mediterranean: it prefers warmer waters and is only occasionally found on northern European coasts such as those of the British Isles. It is up to 500 kg (1,100 lb) in weight and 3 m (10 ft) in length. The largest specimen ever caught weighed 900 kg (1,980 lb). The Tuna is a predator and is one of the largest sea fishes. In the Mediterranean it was caught for food in ancient times. Very little is known about its reproductive biology and nothing of its eggs or fry. The smaller *Thunnus saliens* is found on the coasts of California and weighs up to 125 kg (275 lb).

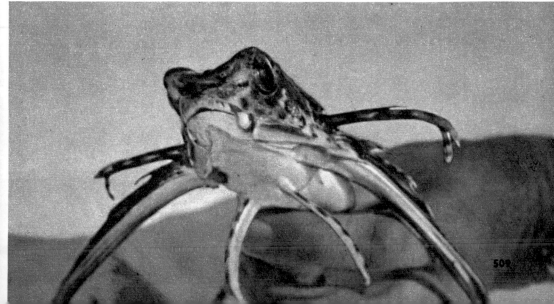

784

The Flatfishes **(Pleuronectiformes)** are well-known food fishes. Fully grown Flatfishes are distinguished by their asymmetrical body, the eyes being found only on the upper side, while the underside of the body has no pigmentation. However, the embryos of Flatfishes are, like their fry, symmetrically structured: but during the course of their development one eye moves from one side of the head over to the other. The gill openings become narrower while the unpaired fins grow longer, and in some species the dorsal,

tail, and anal fins are all joined together to form a sort of frill around the whole body. Flatfishes swim on their sides. Their scales are either ctenoid or cycloid and there is no swim-bladder. More than 400 different species are known. Most of them live in sea water and only a few move up into rivers. They are carnivorous, benthonic fishes which feed on small invertebrates of the sea bed, especially molluscs and, when young, plankton. The quantity of Flatfishes caught in the whole world amounts to about two per cent of the total catch of edible fishes each year. The order Pleuronectiformes is divided into two suborders with several families.

In the family **Bothidae** – the Turbots and Brills – the eyes are usually set on the left side of the body. The dorsal fin as a rule begins just above the broad mouth which stretches over almost a third of the head. The genus *Scophthalmus* contains a number of species, among them the **Turbot**, *Scophthalmus maximus* [785], which is found in the coastal waters of Europe from the Black Sea to the North Sea and less commonly the Baltic. It grows to a length of up to 1 m (3 ft) and weighs up to 16 kg (35 lb). Its scaleless body is covered with rounded knobs.

785

The Turbot grows very slowly. The adults feed on other fishes. The quantity of eggs expelled from the body during spawning reaches the incredible number of about 10,000,000. These fishes spawn in the North Sea from April to August at a depth of between 10 and 40 m (32–128 ft). *Scophthalmus maeoticus* [787] lives on the shallow coasts of the Black Sea. It is up to 85 cm (34 in) in length, 15 kg (33 lb) in weight and can be found at depths of 90–100 m (300–330 ft). In summer, however, it prefers to move in closer to the coast. The male is smaller than the female and one act of spawning will give rise to anything between 3,000,000 and 13,000,000 eggs.

The **Megrim** or **Whiff**, *Lepidorhombus whiffiagonis* (syn. *Rhombus megastomus*) [786], is found in Inshore waters from Iceland to the Mediterranean, where it achieves a length of about 60 cm (24 in). The back is yellowish while the underneath is an off-white colour. Both eyes arc on the left side of the body, and the mouth is large with several pointed teeth.

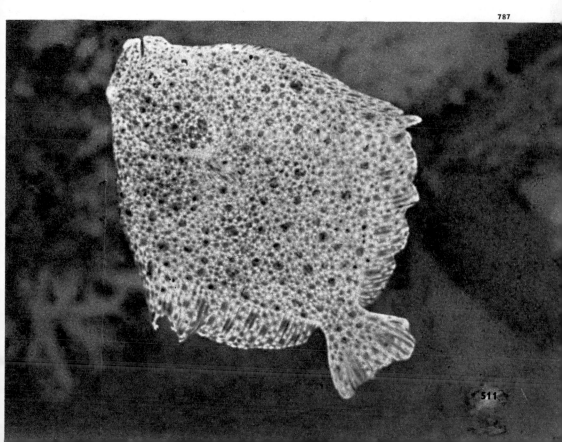

788
789

The **Plaices** and **Dabs (Pleuronectidae)** have symmetrical fins. Their eggs have no oil globule. The best-known genus is *Pleuronectes* which is characterized by a small mouth. The body is covered with cycloid scales. The dorsal fin begins above the eyes.

The **Flounder,** *Platichthys flesus* [788], has small spines at the roots of the fin rays of the dorsal and anal fins. The star-shaped bony plates under the front part of the lateral lines change towards the tail into ctenoid scales. The Flounder is found along the coasts of Europe from the Black Sea through to the eastern part of the Barents Sea. Since it also survives quite well in fresh water it is sometimes found some distance upstream from the mouth of rivers. It spawns in the sea, however, and has also become naturalized in the Caspian Sea. There are a number of subspecies or geographical variations. It grows to a length of 40–50 cm (16-20 in). At each spawning the number of eggs amounts to between 400,000 and 2,000,000. When they first emerge the fry are transparent. Small specimens

are occasionally kept in aquaria. Picture 789 shows one of these fishes buried in sand with only its head and eyes visible. Like all Flatfishes the Flounder is able to change its colouring according to the bed on which it is lying – a good example of the adaptive coloration so common among fishes.

One of the most important Flatfishes of the north Atlantic is the **Plaice,** *Pleuronectes platessa* [790]. Its small scales are rooted firmly and deeply in the skin and the eyes are on the right side of the body. This fish migrates little, grows only slowly, and is 80 cm (32 in) long. However, since the Plaice remains almost permanently in one area there is a danger of over-fishing: certain stretches of water may become so depleted that the population is then difficult to replace. The breeding season extends from January to March and important spawning areas lie in the North Sea, east of the Dogger Bank. The fry feed on plankton and tiny shrimps during the first thirty to forty days of life. Thereafter they lose their symmetrical body shape and grow into the familiar flat shape of sea-

bed fishes. However, as elsewhere in nature, the exception here proves the rule. Some young Plaice depart from the custom of their species by moving their eyes to the left side of the body so that they swim the other way up. These specimens, known as reversed examples, grow quite normally.

If the fish is swimming along in a straight line in the open water it lies in a vertical position and moves its anal and dorsal fins [791]. However, if it wishes to move up to the surface of the water it has to overcome the whole body weight: using its tail fin, it swims with wave-like motions of the

792

whole body [792]. The top of the Plaice is brown or black, and in lighter coloured specimens there are large and small red-yellow flecks over the whole body and arranged in rows along the dorsal and anal fins. Other specimens have a grey marbled colouring.

The large flatfish shown in picture 793 is a **Halibut** (*Hippoglossus hippoglossus*). This fish is lying with its white underside uppermost; the upper surface is a dark olive-green. This is a relatively small Halibut, for specimens weighing up to 320 kg (700 lb) have been caught. It is a predatory fish feeding on smaller fishes, as its powerful jaws and large teeth suggest. In addition to those species so far mentioned the **Sole**, *Solea solea*, which is 60 cm (24 in) long, is also of great economic importance. It is a member of the family **Soleidae** and is a native of all coasts of Europe from the Black Sea to the North Sea.

794

The Spiny Eels, order **Mastacembeliformes**, have fused dorsal and anal fins making a continuous fringe; there are three spines at the front of the anal fin; pelvic fins are absent. The swim-bladder is not connected to the gut. Nasal openings are located on a fleshy, tube-like extension of the mouth.

The family **Mastacembelidae** lives in the waters of equatorial Africa and southern Asia. Two genera are recognized, divided into over thirty species. The **Lesser Spiny Eel**, *Macrognathus aculeatus* [794], lives in India, the whole of southern Asia, some islands of the Malayan Archipelago, and the Moluccas. In the members of the genus *Macrognathus* the dorsal and anal fins are placed far back along the body. These fishes live in fresh and brackish waters and grow to a length of 35 cm (14 in). The

795

516

females are larger than the males and they are already mature when they reach a length of 12 to 15 cm (5–6 in). The mouth and gills are small. The Spiny Eels spend the day in hiding and only emerge towards evening. They feed principally on worms and small animals among the fauna of the river bed. Picture 795 shows a detail of the head with its tube-like nasal extension. This fish has been imported since 1912 and is occasionally kept in aquaria.

The order of Suckerfishes or Remoras **(Echeneiformes)** consists of fishes whose first dorsal fin has been transformed into an oval sucking disc set with lamellae. The scales are cycloid in form and the abdominal fins are arranged, as in the Perches, directly beneath the pectoral fins.

The members of the family **Echeneidae** have a long slender body and small scales. The second dorsal fin is long and symmetrical; underneath is situated an equally long anal fin. There are about ten species, living in warm seas. Occasionally these fishes are encountered in the Mediterranean or even on the southern coasts of England. They attach themselves to other fishes, Turtles, Sharks, Rays, and Whales by means of their suckling pad, and they act as cleaner fishes for their host as well as preying on small fishes and crustaceans.

The **Slender Suckerfish**, *Echeneis naucrates* [796], grows to a length of 1 m (3 ft). Its eggs are pelagic.

They are used by native fishermen for hunting large Turtles In places as far apart as the Caribbean Sea, around Zanzibar, the Torres Strait, and the north coast of Australia.

They attach themselves firmly to the shell of the Turtle so that the fisherman is able to haul both fish and Turtle into his boat by means of a line attached to the tail of the fish. This demonstrates the enormous adhesive power of the sucking pad, whose structure is shown in picture 797. At the same time, however, they have been regarded with some apprehension for an ancient writer claimed that several adult Remoras could deflect a small sailing boat from its course by attaching themselves to it.

The order **Tetraodontiformes** includes the Triggerfishes, Filefishes, Leatherjackets, Cowfishes, and Pufferfishes. In all these fishes the bones of the gill covers are reduced in various ways. The bones in the region of the pelvic fins are absent as are the pelvic fins themselves, although they may be transformed into spines. In some species a sac is formed by a protrusion of the intestine; this is filled with water or air when the fishes puff up their bodies. The gill clefts are small and the scales rough or even spiny. Sometimes the body is covered with bony plates which form a sort of armour. There are either one or two dorsal fins of which the first usually possesses spines. Most species of this order are sea dwellers of tropical and subtropical waters; only a few are found in the rivers of warmer regions.

The family **Triodontidae** is characterized by a long conical snout. The monotypic genus *Triodon* is remarkable for the enormous flap of skin on its ventral surface. It has cutting teeth typical of the Tetraodontiformes. Both the pelvic fins and the spiny dorsal fins are absent. The body is covered with small, spiny plates.

Triodon bursarius [798] comes from the Indo-Malayan archipelago. It is able to open its gullet and fill it

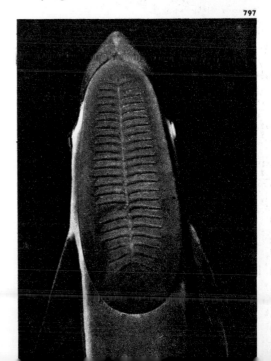

798

This family, too, has pronounced cutting teeth, almost rabbit-like in shape. Its first dorsal fin consists of between one and there spines, while the pelvic fin, if it is present, consists of a single spine. More than thirty species are known. For the most part the Balistidae are relatively small, brightly coloured fishes which exceptionally reach a length of 90 cm (36 in). In each jaw there are eight powerful chisel-like teeth with which the fish breaks off pieces of coral, mussels, and other invertebrates, and consumes the soft body parts. It also feeds on echinoderms which are generally left unmolested by fishes. The Triggerfishes do considerable damage to cultures of Pearl Oysters. They prefer shallow water around coral reefs. Several species are known to sleep on their sides on the sea bottom. Other species dig holes in the sand before spawning in which they protect their eggs before the emergence

with water, thus enormously increasing its size. The Triggerfishes of the family **Balistidae** are found in the Atlantic, the Indian, and the Pacific oceans.

799

of the fry. Although they are very active they are easy to keep in the aquarium.

Balistes vetula [799] is a common fish off the coast of Florida. The basic colouring of its body is yellow to grey-brown of varying intensity with a row of shimmering blue bands on the head and on the fins. A number of black stripes radiate from around the eyes. In fully grown, sexually mature specimens the soft dorsal fin and the tail fin end in a thread-like process. These fishes grow to a length of almost 50 cm (20 in). On the coasts of Brazil they are sometimes eaten but since their flesh is said to have an unpleasant taste if boiled they are always fried.

800

The **Picasso Fish,** *Rhinecanthus aculeatus* [800], one of the best-known Triggerfishes, lives in the Indo-Pacific region where it prefers places with calm water and sandy bottoms.

Certainly one of the most attractive species is *Balistoides conspicillum*, whose body is covered with a network of black lines.

801

802

It comes from the Indo-Pacific region, especially from the waters around South Africa, the Maldives and Ceylon. On the belly, tail, and sides it has large, round, white or bluish spots. The lips are orange to red [Pl. 63]. This extraordinarily active fish is seldom met with in aquaria although it is much sought after.

The **Yellow-spot Triggerfish,** *Pseudobalistes fuscus* [801], also comes from the Indo-Pacific region and the Red Sea. The young are yellow in colouring and have a thick network of blue stripes. If the fish is startled it turns black. It lives singly on the sandy bottom in deep water and feeds on echinoderms and tube worms.

The **Red-toothed Filefish,** *Odonus niger* [802], is very common in the Indian and Pacific oceans and of all Triggerfishes It Is one of the most frequent aquarium species. It is a peaceable fish and when in danger tries to hide. It grows to a length of about 50 cm (20 in). Its basic colouring is a variable shade of green, or even blue or black. The teeth are generally orange-coloured or red.

The tropical zones of all seas are inhabited by the **Black Filefish,** *Melichthys ringens* [803], a species which is regarded by some authors merely as a colour variation of *Melichthys piceus*. Its body colour is dark green to black. At the root of the dorsal and anal fins there is a striking, long, white stripe which makes the fish easily identifiable. The Black Filefish, like many other Pufferfishes, sleeps on its side.

Members of the family **Monacanthidae** (Leatherjackets) are encountered in all warm seas and are usually found living among algae. Some species when they feel threatened dive head first into the plants and are difficult to pick out from their surroundings. They feed mainly on coral polyps. The body is leaf-shaped and greatly compressed at the sides. The most common aquarium species Is the **Spotted Leatherjacket,** *Amanses pardalis* [804], which comes from the Red Sea. The spine of the first dorsal fin is situated immediately above the front edge of the eye. In captivity it will feed on algae, tubifex worms, white worms, mosquito larvae, snails, earthworms and meal worms.

The Cowfishes or Boxfishes of the family **Ostracionidae** have neither dorsal nor pelvic fins and lack bones in the region of the pelvic fins. These fishes live in the warm zones of all seas. Underneath the skin there is a heavy armour of hard bony plates from which only the tail, the dorsal and anal fins, and the mouth protrude. If the fish is frightened it bends its tail round to lie pointing forwards along the body. In some species the armour plating of bone forms a triangular or

805

rectangular box. The Boxfishes feed on small bottom-living animals which they seek among sand and stones. They swim by means of paddling movements of the dorsal and tail fins. The pectoral fins are used to assist the fish in breathing since the gill covers are almost immobile and the gill clefts are narrow. More than thirty species of Boxfishes are known. These fishes are apparently able to release toxins when handled.

The **Long-horned Cowfish**, *Ostracion cornutus* (syn. *Lactophrys cornutus*, *Lactoria cornuta*) [805],

lives pelagically in the Indian and Pacific oceans. It grows to a length of 50 cm (20 in). It is yellow-orange or occasionally olive-green with a turquoise mark on each of the bony plates covering its body. The four horns are characteristic: two are situated above the eyes and point forwards, and two beside the anal fin point backwards.

The bony armour of the **Thorn-backed Boxfish**, *Ostracion gibbosus* [806], which forms a typically triangular shape. The fish is present in the Indo-Pacific region and grows to a length of 30 cm (12 in).

806

The brightly coloured **Freckled Boxfish**, *Ostracion lentiginosus* [807], which lives in the same area as the Thorn-backed Boxfish is brown, green, or blue in colour. Some of the freckles on its body are red, while others are pink to white.

The Pufferfishes (**Tetraodontidae**) have no such armour plating. Their skin is scaleless but lined with small bony plates, often with spines on them. The intestine of these fishes has a number of sacs which the creature is able to fill with water or air so that it can puff itself up to such an enormous size that it looks like a large balloon. The gill arches are reduced to three in number. Members of the genus *Tetraodon* live in tropical seas but also in the rivers of Africa and India. More than sixty species are known. They will eat almost anything that can be chiseled off with their sharp teeth, including seaweed, coral, tunicates, and sponges. Some species spawn in the inter-tidal zone along the coasts.

The **Green Pufferfish**, *Tetraodon fluviatilis*, lives in sea water, fresh water and brackish water in southern India, Ceylon, Burma, Thailand, the

Malayan Peninsula, and the East Indies. Picture 808 shows a young fish about 7 cm (3 in) long. When adult it reaches a length of 17 cm (7 in). Its interesting habits and bright colouring make it a popular species for keeping in aquaria. In captivity it feeds mainly on water snails. The eggs are laid on stones and protected by the male who also cares for the young fry after he has transferred them to a sandy nest. The young are entirely peace-loving although older specimens become rather aggressive. There are great variations in colouring: the body may be flecked or there may be dark, vertical stripes across the back. The belly is white or often grey, sometimes with darker blotches, in adults.

Tetraodon palembangensis [809] lives in the fresh waters of Thailand, Sumatra, and Borneo. This fish is 20 cm (8 in) long. In body shape it resembles the Green Pufferfish. The back is generally lemon-yellow to dark green while the underside is white to yellowish. The back and the flanks are covered with characteristic black markings. It does not get on well either with members of its own species or with other fishes.

809
810

Tetraodon somphongsi [810] comes from the fresh waters of Thailand. This Pufferfish was first described by Klausewitz in 1957. It is not known how large this fish is in its natural surroundings. To date specimens kept in aquaria have not grown beyond 7 cm. This species tolerates some species but not others. It has been successfully bred in captivity.

Tetraodon schoutedeni [811] is an exclusively fresh-water fish which comes from Africa, especially from the lower course of the river Congo. The female is 8 cm (3 in) long and the male somewhat smaller. The sides of the body are bright ochre in colouring, while the back is somewhat darker. It is covered with a number of sepia and black spots which are concentrated in large numbers on the back. The eye is an iridescent red. This Pufferfish can co-exist peacefully with almost any other species. Its diet is restricted to small, thin-shelled snails and other molluscs and it prefers white worms and tubifex worms, although it will also bite at water plants without actually eating them. The flesh of members of the genus *Tetraodon* is tasteless, lean, jelly-like and, like the internal organs, highly poisonous. The genus *Sphaeroides* is regarded by some authors as belonging to a separate family, **Lagocephalidae**. Its most important anatomical features, however, correspond to those of the family Tetraodontidae. The body is long and conical in shape. Some species rest peacefully on their flattened bellies in the sand or even dig themselves in.

61a Siamese Fighting Fish *(Betta splendens)*
61b Giant Gourami *(Colisa fasciata)*

62   Honey Gourami *(Colisa chuna)*

63   *Balistoides conspicillum*

64a   Dwarf Croaking Gourami (*Trichopsis pumilus*)
64b   *Arothron citrinellus*

The **Southern Puffer** or **Swell Toad,** *Sphaeroides spengleri* [812], is olive-brown in colouring when adult, with a number of light green or blue blotches which are scattered over the whole body. These fishes are frequently found near the coasts of the West Indies, Texas, Florida, and southwards to Rio de Janeiro; they are also found in Madeira and the Canary Islands. It is therefore the most widely distributed species of the Tetraodontidae.

The **Black-spotted Blowfish,** *Arothron diadematus* [813], is also included by some authors in the family Lagocephalidae under the designation *Amblyrhynchotes diadematus.* Le Danois regarded it as identical with the species known as *Ovoides nigropunctatus* (syn. *Arothron nigropunctatus*) and he therefore included it in the family Tetraodontidae. Fraser-Brunner examined the skull structure of this species and confirmed that it is in fact properly

813

regarded as a member of the family Tetraodontidae. Clark and Gohar later established a close relationship between this species and *Arothron nigropunctatus* but established certain important distinguishing features. *Arothron diadematus* is a dirty green colour. A broad, dark brown or black band runs from the

forehead across the eyes to the root of the tail fin and broadens considerably along the sides. Around the mouth there is a black ring. The snout is lighter in colouring and so are the cheeks. This species lives in the Red Sea, while the related species *Arothron nigropunctatus* is distributed throughout

814

815

the whole Indo-Pacific region. *Arothron diadematus* can be fed in the aquarium on shrimps and ox heart but will also take, if somewhat reluctantly, meal worms, earthworms, and snails.

The **White-spotted Blowfish**, *Arothron hispidus* [814], which is a native of the waters around the Seychelles and the whole of the Indo-Pacific, is a very active fish. The back is grey or dirty brownish-green, with blue and white spots. The belly is lighter in colouring and crossed with a number of stripes. Around the root of the pectoral fins and the gill clefts there is a yellow, circular pattern. Their favourite food in captivity consists of shrimps but they will also take molluscs and other animal food.

Arothron stellatus, the **Starry Blowfish**, which is occasionally imported, grows astonishingly quickly and is up to 90 cm (36 in) long. It, too, is widely distributed throughout the Indo-Pacific region, although it is comparatively rare. Its body is light in colour with dark spots. The gaily coloured

Arothron citrinellus [Pl. 64b] is an intense, almost shining yellow or orange. Specimens of this species up to 35 cm (14 in) long have been caught around the Seychelles, and in recent years it has been on view in European aquaria.

The **Canthigasteridae** (Tobies) are closely related to the Blowfishes. These fishes live in the warmest parts of the Indo-Pacific and are always very striking. They swim in much the same way as the Balistidae. There is only one genus, *Canthigaster*. The **Ocellated Toby**, *Canthigaster margaritatus* [815], is commonly kept in aquaria. Its basic colouring is fawn with attractive, pearl-like blue flecks and bands which run right down into the orange-coloured tail fin. The eyes move independently of one another and are surrounded by blue rays. They are incredibly nervous creatures. Like the Pufferfishes to which they are more or less closely related, they eat snails and almost any living or dead meat which they can find in the aquarium. They thus serve to keep the water of the aquarium clean and free from pollution.

817

The skin of the Porcupine-fishes (**Diodontidae**) is covered with powerful spines which have a triangular base. In some genera (e. g. *Diodon*) they can be erected while in others (e. g. *Chilomycterus*) they are immovable. There are about sixty species, the most familiar of which – *Diodon hystrix* [818] – is up to 70 cm (28 in) long. Picture 816 shows a Porcupine-fish which was caught off the Cuban coast with a harpoon. The fish has pumped itself full of water and air so that it looks like an enormous spiny ball. It is found in the warm zones of all oceans. There are only two teeth in the mouth, one in the upper and one in the lower jaw. Most members of the genus *Diodon* are poisonous. Their spines can cause very painful wounds which take a long time to heal.

There is a close resemblance especially in younger specimens between *Diodon holacanthus* [817] and *Diodon hystrix*. It grows to a length of 30–60 cm (12–24 in) and is present in all warm seas and is also present on the coasts of Florida, California, and the Hawaiian Islands.

The **Burr-fish,** *Chilomycterus schoepfi* [819], is sometimes brought to Europe for the benefit of aquarists. It lives principally around Florida although it is also found further north, in the Gulf Stream, as far as Cape Cod. Its spines are short and immovable. It has a grey-green back with a number of wavy, longitudinal stripes. Behind the pectoral fins there is a large dark mark. This fish grows to a length of 25 cm (10 in). Young specimens have two horns over the eyes which shrink in later life. As food it particularly likes fairy shrimps and *Mysis*

but will also eat crabs, molluscs, tubifex worms, insect larvae of all species, and whiteworms. In the aquarium it is tame and peaceful.

The Sunfishes of the family **Molidae** have a compressed body which looks as if it has been cut short. This appearance results from the great reduction of the tail. There is no swim-bladder. They have high dorsal and anal fins which are joined to one another in the region of the tail fin. The skin is very thick and tough, scaleless, and rather like thin blubber.

818

819

The **Sunfish,** *Mola mola* [820], is 2.5 m (8 ft) long and has a height of more than 2 m (6 ft). It weighs anything up to 1,000 kg (1 ton). It feeds on zooplankton including small fishes. This creature often swims close to the surface of the water so that its tall dorsal fin sticks out above the surface. Sometimes, however, it lies on its side and allows itself to be carried along by the waves. Nevertheless it

820

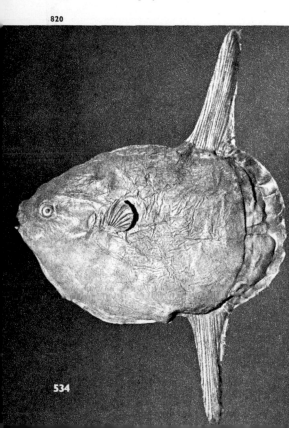

is also able to dive to great depths. At each spawning up to 300,000,000 eggs are produced. The fry live at great depths in the open sea – they are bathypelagic. They have powerful spines which protect them from predatory fishes but these gradually disappear as the Sunfish matures. This species lives in tropical and subtropical seas, although it occasionally occurs on temperature coasts, and is of no great economic significance.

The Clingfishes (order **Gobiesociformes**) are small fishes with soft rayed dorsal and anal fins. They have well-developed pectoral fins. On the underside of the fish there is a sucking organ formed from a modified pelvic fin skeleton and the lower elements of the pectoral fins and the bones of the pectoral girdle. More than 500 species of this order are known, distributed in the various seas of the world. They are all small fishes which for the most part live under stones in coastal waters, although some are found in deep water, and others in fresh water. The sucking disc on the underside of the body enables the Clingfishes to attach themselves to various objects and so resist the force of even the most powerful surf.

The genus *Lepadogaster* is found on the European coasts of the Mediterranean, in the Black Sea, and northwards to the coasts of Great Britain. Some species are occasionally kept in aquaria, for example the **Shore Clingfish,** *Lepadogaster lepadogaster* [821]. It grows to a length of 10–12 cm (4–5 in) and has a well-developed fringe of skin above the nasal openings. The broad head with two blue markings running into one another at the back of the head is characteristic of this species, and they have a pattern which makes them look as if

821

they are wearing yellow or dark brown tinted spectacles. In captivity this fish can be fed on tubifex worms.

The last order is the **Lophiiformes** (Anglerfishes). The front part of the body is very broad and powerfully developed. The gill openings are small. The body is covered with warts and growths of skin so that the fishes resemble stalks of seaweed. The pelvic fins are modified as organs of locomotion. The spiny part of the dorsal fin is placed forward on to the head and appears either as row of separate unbranched rays or is entirely absent. Anglerfishes live in the seas of tropical and temperate zones. They move very little for they are poor swimmers and usually live on the bottom or close under the surface of the water among seaweed where they lurk for prey. Three suborders and several families are recognized.

Of the family **Lophiidae** the **Angler** or **Monkfish**, *Lophius piscatorius* [822], lives on the coasts of Europe. It is up to 1.5 m (5 ft) long and has an extraordinarily broad and flattened head. The eyes are on the upper side of the head, while the mouth is extremely broad and the body scaleless. The first three rays of the dorsal fin are quite independent of one another and form long threads. The first fin ray has a fleshy flap, the movement of which lures other fishes within reach of its mouth. The colouring of its body is fully adapted to the environment in which it lives. The fringe-like growths about the mouth and along the sides enable it to resemble clumps of seaweed, thus greatly improving its camouflage. During the spawning season it makes its way to depths as great as 2,000 m (6,500 ft). It lays its eggs in the form of a wide gelatinous carpet 30–100 cm (12–40 in) broad and 7–16 m (22–52 ft) long. Owing to the fatty content of the eggs this whole mass floats slowly to the surface. The fry are dark in colouring and live pelagically. However, at the age of about four months the fishes change to a benthonic life. On the coasts of England about 2,000 tons of Monkfish are caught each year.

822

823

The Frogfishes (family **Antennariidae**) are mainly pelagic fish living in tropical seas amongst floating seaweed. They are small, high-backed creatures and are able in form and colouring to take on a striking

824

similarity to the seaweed which surrounds them. Members of this family also lure their prey towards them with a worm-like growth at the back of the head.

Of the known species of the genera *Antennarius* and *Histrio* only a few are occasionally kept in aquaria. The **Smooth Fishing-frog** or **Marbled Angler,** *Histrio histrio* (formerly *Antennarius marmoratus*), is present in all tropical seas, where it lives in tangles of seaweed. It builds nests of seaweed and filaments consisting of a secretion of its kidneys. The eggs hang from these filaments in clusters. *Antennarius drombus* [823] is usually brownish-green in colouring and is a frequent catch around the Hawaiian Islands.

Members of the genus *Antennarius* [824] have apparently jointed pectoral fins which are adapted for locomotion among the coral and algae in which they live. The skin is scaleless and coloured yellow to red with brown or black spots. The individual species are difficult to differentiate from each other. A particularly small species for example, is *Antennarius bigibbus* which is known from Mauritius, Madagascar, southern India, Micronesia, Polynesia, the Hawaiian Islands, and the Gulf of California: it is only about 4 cm (1½ in) long. One of the largest species on the other hand, with a length of up to 15 cm (6 in), is *Antennarius leprosus* from the Hawaiian Islands. Since the colouring is so variable it is difficult to give a more precise description of species kept in aquaria, especially when no information is available about their place of origin.

INDEX

ACKNOWLEDGEMENTS

Heather Angel, Biophotos; E. Balon;
P. Chlupaty – W. Weeber; M. Chvojka;
Bruce Coleman Ltd.; V. Elek; S. Frank;
H.-J. Franke; P. Glockner; J. Holčík; William
J. Howes, Angling Photo Service; I. Hrdý;
Keystone Press Agency Ltd.; M. Kocar;
Frank W. Lane; V. Máka; J. Maťák; E. Opatrný;
Photo Aquàtics; V. J. Staněk; S. Štochl;
J. Vostradovský; W. Weiss; R. Zukal.